The Open University

M208 Pure Mathematics

# LA2

GW00643066

# Linear equations and matrices

The Open University, Walton Hall, Milton Keynes, MK7 6AA.

First published 2006.

Edited, designed and typeset by The Open University, using the Open University TeX System.

Printed and bound in the United Kingdom by Hobbs the Printers Limited, Brunel Road, Totton, Hampshire SO40 3WX.

ISBN 0 7492 0223 8

1.1

# Contents

# Introduction

Systems of simultaneous linear equations arise frequently in mathematics and in many other areas. For example, in Unit LA1 you found the point of intersection of a pair of non-parallel lines in $\mathbb{R}^2$ by solving the two equations of the lines as simultaneous equations—that is, by finding the values for $x$ and $y$ that simultaneously satisfy *both* equations. In particular, you found the solution to the system of simultaneous linear equations

$$\begin{cases} 3x - y = \phantom{-}1, \\ \phantom{3}x - y = -1, \end{cases}$$

to be $x = 1$, $y = 2$. In other words, the two lines $3x - y = 1$ and $x - y = -1$ intersect at the point $(1, 2)$.

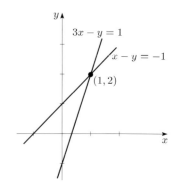

The solution to a system of simultaneous linear equations in two unknowns ($x$ and $y$) corresponds to the points of intersection (if any) of lines in $\mathbb{R}^2$. Similarly, solutions to systems of linear equations in three unknowns correspond to the intersection (if any) of planes in $\mathbb{R}^3$. Although systems with more unknowns can be thought of in relation to intersections in spaces of higher dimension, we develop a strategy for solving such systems without the need to visualise a multi-dimensional world!

Recall from Unit LA1, Subsection 1.2, that an equation of the form $2x + 3y + 4z = 5$ represents a plane in $\mathbb{R}^3$.

Matrices appear throughout mathematics. In this unit we assume no prior knowledge of matrices, although you may well have met them before. We use matrices as a concise way of representing systems of linear equations, and then go on to study matrix algebra and determinants. Throughout this unit we relate our results to the solutions of systems of simultaneous linear equations. Many of the ideas and methods introduced here will be used in the following three units on linear algebra.

In Section 1 we begin by considering simultaneous linear equations in two and three unknowns. We introduce the idea of a *solution set*, and interpret our results geometrically. We then generalise these ideas to systems of $m$ simultaneous linear equations in $n$ unknowns, and introduce the method of *Gauss–Jordan elimination* to solve them systematically.

In Section 2 we develop a strategy for solving systems of linear equations, based on performing *elementary row operations* on the *augmented matrix* of the system in question. We transform the augmented matrix to *row reduced* form, from which we can easily read off any solutions. This method is algorithmic, and a computer can be programmed to perform it; this enables large systems with many unknowns to be handled efficiently.

Most computer programs use a slightly modified version of this method.

In Section 3 we study the algebra of matrices. We investigate the addition and scalar multiplication of matrices, and see that matrices can be thought of as a generalisation of vectors. We use the dot product of vectors to define the multiplication of one matrix by another. Finally, we introduce some important types of matrices, and the matrix operation of *transposition*—interchanging the rows and columns of a matrix—which will be used later in the block.

In Section 4 we introduce the *inverse* of a matrix. This plays a role in matrix arithmetic similar to that of the reciprocal of a number in ordinary arithmetic. We show that many matrices do not have inverses, and give a method for finding an inverse when it does exist. We also link the idea of the *invertibility* of a matrix with the number of solutions of some systems of linear equations.

In Section 5 we use systems of linear equations to introduce the *determinant* of a square matrix. The determinant assigns to each square matrix a number which characterises certain properties of the matrix. In particular, we prove that a matrix is invertible if and only if its determinant is non-zero; this provides a method for determining whether or not a given matrix is invertible.

# Study guide

Sections 1 to 5 should be studied in the natural order.

Section 1 is straightforward and should not take you long.

Section 2 is the audio section. Using *row-reduction* to solve systems of linear equations is an important method to master.

Much of Section 3 may be revision for you. If you have not multiplied matrices before, then you will need to spend some time practising this as it may seem strange at first. Matrix multiplication plays an important part in the remainder of the block.

Sections 4 and 5 both contain important material. There is a lot of theory in these sections, and you need not master it completely. You should, however, make sure that you can find the inverse and evaluate the determinant of a $2 \times 2$ or $3 \times 3$ matrix, and you should at least read the statements of the theorems.

# 1   Simultaneous linear equations

After working through this section, you should be able to:

(a) understand the connection between the solutions of systems of simultaneous linear equations in two and three unknowns and the intersection of lines and planes in $\mathbb{R}^2$ and $\mathbb{R}^3$;

(b) describe the three types of *elementary operation*;

(c) use the method of *Gauss–Jordan elimination* to find the solutions of systems of simultaneous linear equations;

(d) explain the terms *solution set*, *consistent*, *inconsistent* and *homogeneous system of simultaneous linear equations*.

## 1.1  Systems in two and three unknowns

### Systems in two unknowns

### One equation

Recall that an equation of the form

$$ax + by = c$$

represents a line in $\mathbb{R}^2$. There are infinitely many solutions to this equation—one corresponding to each point on the line.

Unit LA1, Subsection 1.1.

Here, $a$, $b$ and $c$ are real numbers, and $a$ and $b$ are not both zero.

## Two equations

The solutions to the system of two simultaneous linear equations

$$\begin{cases} ax + by = c, \\ dx + ey = f, \end{cases}$$

Here, $a, b, \ldots, f$ are real numbers.

in the two unknowns $x$ and $y$ correspond to the points of intersection of these two lines in $\mathbb{R}^2$.

Two arbitrary lines in $\mathbb{R}^2$ may intersect at a unique point, be parallel or coincide. This means that solving a system of two simultaneous linear equations in two unknowns yields exactly one of the following three situations.

Unit LA1, Subsection 1.1.

- There is a unique solution, when the two lines that the equations represent intersect at a unique point.

  For example, the system

  $$\begin{cases} x - y = -1, \\ 2x + y = \phantom{-}4, \end{cases}$$

  has the unique solution $x = 1$, $y = 2$, corresponding to the unique point of intersection $(1, 2)$ of the two lines in $\mathbb{R}^2$.

- There is no solution, when the two lines that the equations represent are parallel.

  For example, the system

  $$\begin{cases} x - y = -1, \\ x - y = \phantom{-}1, \end{cases}$$

  represents two parallel lines in $\mathbb{R}^2$, which do not intersect, and so has no solutions.

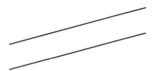

- There are infinitely many solutions, when the two lines that the equations represent coincide.

  For example, the system

  $$\begin{cases} -6x + 3y = -6, \\ \phantom{-}2x - \phantom{3}y = \phantom{-}2, \end{cases}$$

  has infinitely many solutions, as the two equations represent the same line in $\mathbb{R}^2$. In a sense, the two lines intersect at each of their points; that is, each pair of values for $x$ and $y$ satisfying $2x - y = 2$ is a solution to this system.

## Systems in three unknowns

### One equation

Recall that an equation of the form

$$ax + by + cz = d$$

Unit LA1, Subsection 1.2.

Here, $a$, $b$, $c$ and $d$ are real numbers, and $a$, $b$ and $c$ are not all zero.

represents a plane in $\mathbb{R}^3$. There are infinitely many solutions to this equation—one corresponding to each point in the plane.

## Two equations

The solutions to the system of two simultaneous linear equations

$$\begin{cases} ax + by + cz = d, \\ ex + fy + gz = h, \end{cases}$$

Here, $a, b, \ldots, h$ are real numbers.

in the three unknowns $x$, $y$ and $z$ correspond to the points of intersection of these two planes in $\mathbb{R}^3$.

Two arbitrary planes in $\mathbb{R}^3$ may intersect, be parallel or coincide. In general, when two distinct planes in $\mathbb{R}^3$ intersect, the set of common points is a line that lies in both planes. This means that solving a system of two simultaneous linear equations in three unknowns yields exactly one of the following two situations.

Unit LA1, Subsection 1.2.

- There is no solution, when the two planes that the equations represent are parallel.

  For example, the system

  $$\begin{cases} x + y + z = 1, \\ x + y + z = 2, \end{cases}$$

  represents two parallel planes in $\mathbb{R}^3$ and so has no solutions.

- There are infinitely many solutions, when the two planes that the equations represent coincide, or when they intersect in a line.

  For example, the system

  $$\begin{cases} x + y + z = 1, \\ 2x + 2y + 2z = 2, \end{cases}$$

  has infinitely many solutions, as the two equations represent the same plane in $\mathbb{R}^3$. Each set of values for $x$, $y$ and $z$ satisfying $x + y + z = 1$ is a solution to this system, such as $x = 1$, $y = 0$, $z = 0$ and $x = -2$, $y = 4$, $z = -1$.

  Similarly, the system

  $$\begin{cases} x + y + z = 1, \\ x + y = 1, \end{cases}$$

  has infinitely many solutions: the planes in $\mathbb{R}^3$ represented by the two equations intersect in a line. The $z$-coordinate of each point on this line is zero, so the line lies in the $(x, y)$-plane. Each set of values for $x$, $y$ and $z$ satisfying $x + y = 1$ and $z = 0$ is a solution to this system, such as $x = 1$, $y = 0$, $z = 0$ and $x = 5$, $y = -4$, $z = 0$.

## Three equations

In a similar way, the solutions to the system of three simultaneous linear equations

$$\begin{cases} ax + by + cz = d, \\ ex + fy + gz = h, \\ ix + jy + kz = l, \end{cases}$$

Here, $a, b, \ldots, l$ are real numbers.

in the three unknowns $x$, $y$ and $z$ correspond to the points of intersection of these three planes in $\mathbb{R}^3$.

Three arbitrary planes in $\mathbb{R}^3$ may meet each other in a number of different ways. We illustrate these possibilities below.

A system of three simultaneous linear equations in three unknowns yields exactly one of the following three situations.

- There is a unique solution, when the three planes that the equations represent intersect at a unique point.

  For example, the system

  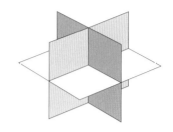

  $$\begin{cases} x + y + z = 1, \\ x + y \quad\;\; = 1, \\ x \quad\quad - z = 0, \end{cases}$$

  has the unique solution $x = 0$, $y = 1$, $z = 0$, corresponding to the unique point of intersection $(0, 1, 0)$ of the three planes in $\mathbb{R}^3$.

- There is no solution, when two of the planes that the equations represent are parallel, or when the three planes form a triangular prism.

  For example, the system

  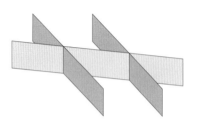

  $$\begin{cases} x + y + z = 1, \\ x + y + z = 2, \\ x + y - z = 0, \end{cases}$$

  represents three planes in $\mathbb{R}^3$, the first two of which are parallel, and so has no solutions.

  Similarly, the system

  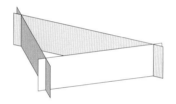

  $$\begin{cases} x + y \quad\;\; = 1, \\ x \quad\;\; + z = 1, \\ \quad - y + z = 1, \end{cases}$$

  has no solutions: the planes in $\mathbb{R}^3$ represented by the three equations intersect in pairs, forming a triangular prism, and so there are no points common to *all three* planes.

- There are infinitely many solutions, when the three planes that the equations represent intersect either in a plane or in a line.

  For example, the system

  $$\begin{cases} x + y + z = 1, \\ -x - y - z = -1, \\ 2x + 2y + 2z = 2, \end{cases}$$

  has infinitely many solutions, as the three equations all represent the same plane in $\mathbb{R}^3$. Each set of values for $x$, $y$ and $z$ satisfying $x + y + z = 1$ is a solution to this system, such as $x = 1$, $y = 0$, $z = 0$ and $x = -1$, $y = 3$, $z = -1$.

  Similarly, the system

  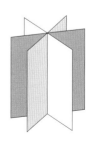

  $$\begin{cases} x + y + z = 1, \\ x + y \quad\;\; = 1, \\ x + y - z = 1, \end{cases}$$

  has infinitely many solutions: the planes in $\mathbb{R}^3$ represented by the three equations intersect in a line. The $z$-coordinate of each point on this line is zero, so the line lies in the $(x, y)$-plane. Each set of values for $x$, $y$ and $z$ satisfying $x + y = 1$ and $z = 0$ is a solution to this system, such as $x = 1$, $y = 0$, $z = 0$ and $x = -5$, $y = 6$, $z = 0$.

# 1.2 Systems in $n$ unknowns

The equations for a line in $\mathbb{R}^2$ and a plane in $\mathbb{R}^3$ are *linear equations* in two and three unknowns, respectively. Similarly, an equation of the form

$$ax + by + cz + dw = e$$

is a linear equation in the four unknowns $x$, $y$, $z$ and $w$. In general, we can define a linear equation in any number of unknowns.

Here, $a, \ldots, e$ are real numbers, and $a$, $b$, $c$ and $d$ are not all zero.

---

**Definitions**   An equation of the form

$$a_1 x_1 + a_2 x_2 + \cdots + a_n x_n = b,$$

where $a_1, a_2, \ldots, a_n, b$ are real numbers, and $a_1, \ldots, a_n$ are not all zero, is a **linear equation** in the $n$ unknowns $x_1$, $x_2$, $\ldots$, $x_n$. The numbers $a_i$ are the **coefficients**, and $b$ is the **constant term**.

---

A linear equation has no terms that are products of unknowns, such as $x_1^2$ or $x_1 x_4$.

**Exercise 1.1**   Which of the following are linear equations in the unknowns $x_1, \ldots, x_5$?

(a)  $x_1 + 3x_2 - x_3 - 5x_4 - 2x_5 = 0$     (b)  $x_1 - x_2 + 2x_3 x_4 + 3x_5 = 4$

(c)  $5x_2 - x_5 = 2$     (d)  $a_1 x_1 + a_2 x_2^2 + \cdots + a_5 x_5^5 = b$

We write a general system of $m$ simultaneous linear equations in $n$ unknowns as

$$\begin{cases} a_{11}x_1 + a_{12}x_2 + \cdots + a_{1n}x_n = b_1, \\ a_{21}x_1 + a_{22}x_2 + \cdots + a_{2n}x_n = b_2, \\ \quad\vdots \qquad\quad \vdots \qquad\qquad\quad \vdots \qquad\quad \vdots \\ a_{m1}x_1 + a_{m2}x_2 + \cdots + a_{mn}x_n = b_m. \end{cases}$$

Frequently, we refer simply to *systems of linear equations*, as the full description is rather a mouthful!

The numbers $b_i$ are the constant terms, the variables $x_i$ are the unknowns and the numbers $a_{ij}$ are the coefficients. We use the double subscript $ij$ to show that $a_{ij}$ is the coefficient of the $j$th unknown in the $i$th equation. The number $m$ of equations need not be the same as the number $n$ of unknowns.

A solution of a system of linear equations is a list of values for the unknowns that simultaneously satisfy each of the equations. In solving a system, we look for *all* the solutions—you have already seen that some systems have infinitely many solutions.

---

**Definitions**   The values $x_1 = c_1, x_2 = c_2, \ldots, x_n = c_n$ are a **solution** of a system of $m$ simultaneous linear equations in $n$ unknowns, $x_1, \ldots, x_n$, if these values simultaneously satisfy all $m$ equations of the system. The **solution set** of the system is the set of all the solutions.

---

For example, you saw earlier that the solution set of the system

$$\begin{cases} x + y + z = 1, \\ x + y \quad\;\; = 1, \\ x \quad\;\; - z = 0, \end{cases} \tag{1.1}$$

is the set $\{(0, 1, 0)\}$, which has just one member.

You also saw that the solution set of the system

$$\begin{cases} x + y + z = 1, \\ x + y + z = 2, \\ x + y - z = 0, \end{cases} \qquad (1.2)$$

is the empty set.

**Definitions**   A system of simultaneous linear equations is **consistent** when it has at least one solution, and **inconsistent** when it has no solutions.

The system (1.1) is consistent, and the system (1.2) is inconsistent.

When a system of linear equations has infinitely many solutions, we can write down a general solution from which all solutions can be found. We illustrate this with an example that you have already met.

You saw earlier that the solutions of the system

$$\begin{cases} x + y + z = 1, \\ x + y \phantom{{}+z} = 1, \\ x + y - z = 1, \end{cases}$$

are the sets of values for $x$, $y$ and $z$ satisfying $x + y = 1$ and $z = 0$. The unknowns $x$ and $y$ are related by the equation $x + y = 1$, which we can rewrite as $y = 1 - x$. Thus for each real parameter $k$ assigned to the unknown $x$, we have a corresponding value $1 - k$ for the unknown $y$. We write this general solution as

$$x = k, \quad y = 1 - k, \quad z = 0, \quad \text{where } k \in \mathbb{R}.$$

To highlight the connection between the solutions of the system and the intersection of the planes in $\mathbb{R}^3$, we can write the solution set as a set of points in $\mathbb{R}^3$:

$$\{(k, 1 - k, 0) : k \in \mathbb{R}\}.$$

The order of the unknowns must be clear—the triples $(1, 0, 0)$ and $(0, 1, 0)$ correspond to different solutions.

## Homogeneous systems

In the following systems of linear equations, the constant terms are all zero:

$$\begin{cases} 2x + 3y = 0, \\ x - y = 0; \end{cases} \qquad (1.3)$$

$$\begin{cases} x - y - z = 0, \\ 2x + y - z = 0, \\ -x + y + z = 0. \end{cases} \qquad (1.4)$$

Such systems are called *homogeneous*.

**Definitions**   A **homogeneous** system of linear equations is a system of simultaneous linear equations in which each constant term is zero.

A system containing at least one non-zero constant term is a **non-homogeneous** system.

If we substitute $x = 0$, $y = 0$ into system (1.3), and $x = 0$, $y = 0$, $z = 0$ into system (1.4), then all the equations are satisfied. These solutions are called *trivial*.

> **Definitions**   The **trivial** solution to a system of simultaneous linear equations is the solution with each unknown equal to zero.
>
> A solution with at least one non-zero unknown is a **non-trivial** solution.

A homogeneous system always has at least the trivial solution, and is therefore always consistent.

*Non-homogeneous systems have only non-trivial solutions.*

**Exercise 1.2**   Write down a general homogeneous system of $m$ linear equations in $n$ unknowns, and show that the solution set contains the trivial solution.

Returning to system (1.4), we see that there are other solutions. For example, $x = 2$, $y = -1$, $z = 3$ is a solution. In fact, this system has an infinite solution set, which we can write as

*System (1.3) has no non-trivial solutions.*

$$\{(2k, -k, 3k) : k \in \mathbb{R}\}.$$

## Number of solutions

We have already seen that when $m \le n \le 3$, a system of $m$ equations in $n$ unknowns has a solution set which

- contains exactly one solution,
- or is empty,
- or contains infinitely many solutions.

In fact, the solution set of a system of $m$ linear equations in $n$ unknowns has one of these forms, for any $m$ and $n$.

*This assertion will be proved in Unit LA4.*

We saw earlier that two non-parallel planes in $\mathbb{R}^3$ cannot intersect in a unique point. A consistent system of two linear equations in three unknowns therefore has an infinite solution set. In general, a consistent system of $m$ equations in $n$ unknowns, with $m < n$, has insufficient constraints on the unknowns to determine them uniquely; that is, it has an infinite solution set.

## 1.3  Solving systems

We now introduce a systematic method for solving systems of simultaneous linear equations. This method is called **Gauss–Jordan elimination**. It entails successively transforming a system into simpler systems, in such a way that the solution set remains unchanged. The process ends when the solutions can be determined easily.

*You will meet this method again in Section 2, where you will use matrices to represent systems of linear equations. A strategy is given there.*

The idea is to reduce the number of unknowns in each equation. In general, we use the first equation to eliminate the first unknown from all the other equations, then use the second equation to eliminate another unknown (usually the second) from all the other equations, and so on.

To avoid confusion when applying this method, we label the current equations $\mathbf{r}_1$, $\mathbf{r}_2$, and so on. We can then write down how we are transforming the preceding system to obtain the current (simpler) system. We use the symbol $\leftrightarrow$ ('interchanges with') to indicate that two equations are to be interchanged; for example, $\mathbf{r}_1 \leftrightarrow \mathbf{r}_2$ means that the first and second equations are interchanged. We use the symbol $\rightarrow$ ('goes to') to show how an equation is to be transformed. For example, $\mathbf{r}_2 \rightarrow \mathbf{r}_2 + \mathbf{r}_1$ means that the second equation of the system is transformed by adding the first equation to it.

*The same notation, $\mathbf{r}_1$, $\mathbf{r}_2$, and so on, will be used in Section 2 where we transform rows of matrices, hence the choice of the letter $\mathbf{r}$.*

We start by illustrating this method with a system of two linear equations in two unknowns. Although this method is not the simplest way of solving this particular system, it proves very useful in solving more complicated systems.

**Example 1.1**    Solve the following system of two linear equations in two unknowns:

$$\begin{cases} 2x + 4y = 10, \\ 4x + \ y = \ 6. \end{cases}$$

**Solution**    We aim to simplify the system by eliminating the unknown $y$ from the first equation and the unknown $x$ from the second. The operations we perform do not alter the solution set of the system.

We label the two equations of the system:

$$\begin{matrix} \mathbf{r}_1 \\ \mathbf{r}_2 \end{matrix} \qquad \begin{cases} 2x + 4y = 10, \\ 4x + \ y = \ 6. \end{cases}$$

We begin by simplifying the first equation; we divide it through by 2, so that the coefficient of $x$ is equal to 1:

$$\mathbf{r}_1 \to \tfrac{1}{2}\mathbf{r}_1 \qquad \begin{cases} x + 2y = 5, \\ 4x + \ y = 6. \end{cases}$$

We then transform this system into a system with no $x$-term in the second equation. To do this, we subtract 4 times the first equation from the second:

$$\mathbf{r}_2 \to \mathbf{r}_2 - 4\mathbf{r}_1 \qquad \begin{cases} x + 2y = \ \ \ 5, \\ \ \ - 7y = -14. \end{cases}$$

We now simplify the second equation of this new system by dividing through by $-7$. This yields a system which already looks less complicated than the original system, but has the same solution set:

$$\mathbf{r}_2 \to -\tfrac{1}{7}\mathbf{r}_2 \qquad \begin{cases} x + 2y = 5, \\ \ \ \ \ \ \ y = 2. \end{cases}$$

We next use this new second equation to eliminate the $y$-term from the first equation. We subtract twice the second equation from the first, which yields the system

$$\mathbf{r}_1 \to \mathbf{r}_1 - 2\mathbf{r}_2 \qquad \begin{cases} x \ \ \ \ \ \ = 1, \\ \ \ \ \ \ \ y = 2. \end{cases}$$

We conclude that there is a unique solution—namely, $x = 1$, $y = 2$.

In calculations of this sort, errors are easily made. It is therefore advisable to check the solution by substituting it back into the equations of the original system. For this example, substituting $x = 1$ and $y = 2$, we find that

$$\begin{cases} (2 \times 1) + (4 \times 2) = 10, \quad \checkmark \\ (4 \times 1) + (1 \times 2) = \ 6. \quad \checkmark \end{cases} \ \blacksquare$$

The steps we performed in this example involve either multiplying (or dividing) an equation by a non-zero number, or changing one equation by adding (or subtracting) a multiple of another. Neither of these operations alters the solution set of the system. Changing the order in which we write down the equations also does not alter the solution set of the system. These are the three operations, called *elementary operations*, that we perform to simplify a system of linear equations when using the method of Gauss–Jordan elimination.

In other words, we aim to reduce the system to the form

$$\begin{cases} x \ \ \ \ \ = *, \\ \ \ \ \ y = *, \end{cases}$$

where the asterisks denote numbers to be determined.

At each step, we relabel (implicitly) the equations of the current system. These two equations therefore become the *new* $\mathbf{r}_1$ and $\mathbf{r}_2$.

> **Elementary operations**    The following operations do not change the solution set of a system of linear equations.
> 1. Interchange two equations.
> 2. Multiply an equation by a non-zero number.
> 3. Change one equation by adding to it a multiple of another.

Operation 2 includes division by a non-zero number.

Operation 3 includes subtracting a multiple of one equation from another.

**Exercise 1.3**    Solve the following system of two linear equations in two unknowns:

$$\begin{cases} x + y = 4, \\ 2x - y = 5, \end{cases}$$

by performing elementary operations to simplify the system as in Example 1.1.

We now solve a system of three linear equations in three unknowns. We use elementary operations to try to reduce the system to the form

$$\begin{cases} x & & = *, \\ & y & = *, \\ & & z = *. \end{cases}$$

Here, the asterisks denote numbers to be determined.

**Example 1.2**    Solve the following system of three linear equations in three unknowns:

$$\begin{cases} x + y + 2z = 3, \\ 2x + 2y + 3z = 5, \\ x - y = 5. \end{cases}$$

**Solution**    We label the three equations of the system:

$$\begin{array}{ll} \mathbf{r}_1 \\ \mathbf{r}_2 \\ \mathbf{r}_3 \end{array} \qquad \begin{cases} x + y + 2z = 3, \\ 2x + 2y + 3z = 5, \\ x - y = 5. \end{cases}$$

We begin the simplification by using the first equation to eliminate the $x$-term from the second and third equations:

$$\begin{array}{ll} \mathbf{r}_2 \to \mathbf{r}_2 - 2\mathbf{r}_1 \\ \mathbf{r}_3 \to \mathbf{r}_3 - \mathbf{r}_1 \end{array} \qquad \begin{cases} x + y + 2z = 3, \\ -z = -1, \\ -2y - 2z = 2. \end{cases}$$

We now have no $y$-term in the second equation, and so cannot use this equation to eliminate the $y$-term from the first and third equations. We also cannot use the first equation to eliminate the $y$-term from the third equation, as this would reintroduce an $x$-term. We therefore interchange the second and third equations, to obtain a non-zero $y$-term in the new second equation:

$$\mathbf{r}_2 \leftrightarrow \mathbf{r}_3 \qquad \begin{cases} x + y + 2z = 3, \\ -2y - 2z = 2, \\ -z = -1. \end{cases}$$

We simplify this new second equation by dividing through by $-2$:

$$\mathbf{r}_2 \to -\tfrac{1}{2}\mathbf{r}_2 \qquad \begin{cases} x + y + 2z = 3, \\ y + z = -1, \\ -z = -1. \end{cases}$$

We can now use the second equation to eliminate the $y$-term from the first equation:

$$\mathbf{r}_1 \to \mathbf{r}_1 - \mathbf{r}_2 \qquad \begin{cases} x & + z = & 4, \\ & y + z = & -1, \\ & - z = & -1. \end{cases}$$

We simplify the third equation by multiplying through by $-1$:

$$\begin{cases} x & + z = & 4, \\ & y + z = & -1, \\ & z = & 1. \end{cases}$$
$$\mathbf{r}_3 \to -\mathbf{r}_3$$

Finally, we use the third equation to eliminate the $z$-term from the first and second equations:

$$\begin{aligned} \mathbf{r}_1 \to \mathbf{r}_1 - \mathbf{r}_3 \\ \mathbf{r}_2 \to \mathbf{r}_2 - \mathbf{r}_3 \end{aligned} \qquad \begin{cases} x & & = & 3, \\ & y & = & -2, \\ & z = & 1. \end{cases}$$

We conclude that there is a unique solution—namely, $x = 3$, $y = -2$, $z = 1$.  ∎

You should check this solution by substituting it into the original equations.

**Exercise 1.4**   Solve the following system of three linear equations in three unknowns:

$$\begin{cases} x + y - z = & 8, \\ 2x - y + z = & 1, \\ -x + 3y + 2z = & -8. \end{cases}$$

Each example solved in this subsection has a unique solution. We now show how to apply the method to a system that does not have a unique solution.

It is not usually possible to reduce a system with an infinite solution set to one where each equation contains just one unknown. This is illustrated by the following example.

**Example 1.3**   Solve the following system of three linear equations in three unknowns:

$$\begin{cases} x + 2y & = & 0, \\ y - z = & 2, \\ x + y + z = & -2. \end{cases}$$

**Solution**   We label the three equations, and apply elementary operations to simplify the system. To save space, we write the explanations to the right of the equations.

$$\begin{aligned} \mathbf{r}_1 \\ \mathbf{r}_2 \\ \mathbf{r}_3 \end{aligned} \qquad \begin{cases} x + 2y & = & 0 \\ y - z = & 2 \\ x + y + z = & -2 \end{cases}$$

We label the equations.

$$\begin{cases} x + 2y & = & 0 \\ y - z = & 2 \\ - y + z = & -2 \end{cases}$$
$$\mathbf{r}_3 \to \mathbf{r}_3 - \mathbf{r}_1$$

We eliminate the $x$-term from $\mathbf{r}_3$ using $\mathbf{r}_1$.

$$\mathbf{r}_1 \to \mathbf{r}_1 - 2\mathbf{r}_2 \qquad \begin{cases} x & + 2z = & -4 \\ y - z = & 2 \\ 0x + 0y + 0z = & 0 \end{cases}$$
$$\mathbf{r}_3 \to \mathbf{r}_3 + \mathbf{r}_2$$

We eliminate the $y$-terms from $\mathbf{r}_1$ and $\mathbf{r}_3$ using $\mathbf{r}_2$.

We have written the current $\mathbf{r}_3$ equation as $0x + 0y + 0z = 0$ to highlight the fact that all the coefficients are zero, although in future examples we shall simply write $0 = 0$. This equation gives no constraints on $x$, $y$ and $z$.

'No constraints' means that any values for $x$, $y$ and $z$ satisfy the equation.

If we were to try to use equation $\mathbf{r}_2$ to eliminate the $z$-term from $\mathbf{r}_1$, we would reintroduce a $y$-term. Similarly, using equation $\mathbf{r}_1$ to eliminate the $z$-term from the equation $\mathbf{r}_2$ would reintroduce an $x$-term.

The system has an infinite solution set, as there are insufficient constraints on the unknowns to determine them uniquely. We have two equations, one relating the unknowns $x$ and $z$, and the other relating $y$ and $z$. As each equation involves a $z$-term, we can choose any value we wish for $z$, and write the general solution as

$x = -4 - 2z$ and $y = 2 + z$.

$$x = -4 - 2k, \quad y = 2 + k, \quad z = k, \quad k \in \mathbb{R}. \quad \blacksquare$$

Whenever the simplification results in an equation $0 = 0$, we have, in effect, reduced the number of equations. We simplify the remaining equations as far as possible, in order to determine the solution set.

**Exercise 1.5**   Solve the following system of three linear equations in three unknowns:
$$\begin{cases} x + 3y - z = 4, \\ -x + 2y - 4z = 6, \\ x + 2y = 2. \end{cases}$$

We now try to solve an inconsistent system.

**Example 1.4**   Solve the following system of three linear equations in three unknowns:
$$\begin{cases} x + 2y + 4z = 6, \\ y + z = 1, \\ x + 3y + 5z = 10. \end{cases}$$

**Solution**   We apply elementary operations to simplify the system.

$$\begin{array}{l} \mathbf{r}_1 \\ \mathbf{r}_2 \\ \mathbf{r}_3 \end{array} \qquad \begin{cases} x + 2y + 4z = 6 \\ y + z = 1 \\ x + 3y + 5z = 10 \end{cases}$$

We label the equations.

$$\begin{array}{l} \\ \\ \mathbf{r}_3 \rightarrow \mathbf{r}_3 - \mathbf{r}_1 \end{array} \qquad \begin{cases} x + 2y + 4z = 6 \\ y + z = 1 \\ y + z = 4 \end{cases}$$

We eliminate the $x$-term from $\mathbf{r}_3$ using $\mathbf{r}_1$.

$$\begin{array}{l} \mathbf{r}_1 \rightarrow \mathbf{r}_1 - 2\mathbf{r}_2 \\ \\ \mathbf{r}_3 \rightarrow \mathbf{r}_3 - \mathbf{r}_2 \end{array} \qquad \begin{cases} x + 2z = 4 \\ y + z = 1 \\ 0 = 3 \end{cases}$$

We eliminate the $y$-terms from $\mathbf{r}_1$ and $\mathbf{r}_3$ using $\mathbf{r}_2$.

Concentrating on the current $\mathbf{r}_3$ equation ($0 = 3$), we see that there are no values of $x$, $y$ and $z$ that satisfy it. The solution set of this system of linear equations is the empty set.   $\blacksquare$

Compare this equation with the final equation $\mathbf{r}_3$ in the solution to Example 1.3.

Whenever the simplification results in an equation $0 = *$, where the asterisk $*$ denotes a non-zero number, we have an inconsistent system, as this equation has no solutions. There is no point in simplifying the remaining equations further. In fact, in Example 1.4, inconsistency of the system could have been inferred at the penultimate stage, as the equations $y + z = 1$ and $y + z = 4$ form an inconsistent system.

**Exercise 1.6**  Solve the following system of three linear equations in three unknowns:

$$\begin{cases} x + y + z = 6, \\ -x + y - 3z = -2, \\ 2x + y + 3z = 6. \end{cases}$$

# 1.4 Applications

Systems of simultaneous linear equations frequently arise when we use mathematics to solve problems; that is, when we formulate a mathematical model to help solve a problem.

In general, to model any straightforward problem we follow the same basic procedure.

1. Identify the unknowns.
2. Analyse each statement of the problem, and rewrite it as an equation relating the unknowns.
3. Solve these equations.
4. Write the solution in words to answer the problem, checking that it 'makes sense'.

These four steps are illustrated in the following example.

**Example 1.5**  The sum of the ages of my sister and my brother is 40 years. My brother is 12 years older than my sister. How old is my sister?

**Solution**  First we decide what the unknowns are. Here we are asked to find the age of my sister, so this is obviously one unknown. The statement relates my sister's age to my brother's age. We do not know my brother's age, so this is a second unknown. These are the only two unknowns in this problem. Let us denote my sister's age by $s$ and my brother's age by $b$ (in years). 

*This is step 1.*

The first statement of the problem now translates to the equation 

*This is step 2.*

$$s + b = 40,$$

and the second statement to

$$b = s + 12.$$

We write these two equations in the usual form:

$$\begin{cases} s + b = 40, \\ -s + b = 12. \end{cases}$$

This system could be solved more simply but, as a further illustration of the method, we apply elementary operations to simplify it. 

*This is step 3.*

$$\begin{array}{ll} \mathbf{r}_1 \\ \mathbf{r}_2 \end{array} \qquad \begin{cases} s + b = 40 \\ -s + b = 12 \end{cases}$$

*We label the equations.*

$$\mathbf{r}_2 \to \mathbf{r}_2 + \mathbf{r}_1 \qquad \begin{cases} s + b = 40 \\ 2b = 52 \end{cases}$$

*We eliminate the $s$-term from $\mathbf{r}_2$ using $\mathbf{r}_1$.*

$$\mathbf{r}_2 \to \tfrac{1}{2}\mathbf{r}_2 \qquad \begin{cases} s + b = 40 \\ b = 26 \end{cases}$$

*We simplify $\mathbf{r}_2$ by dividing through by 2.*

$\mathbf{r}_1 \to \mathbf{r}_1 - \mathbf{r}_2$   $\begin{cases} s \quad\;\; = 14 \\ \quad b = 26 \end{cases}$

Finally, we eliminate the $b$-term from $\mathbf{r}_1$ using $\mathbf{r}_2$.

The system has a unique solution—namely, $s = 14$, $b = 26$.

The answer to the problem is that my sister is 14 years old. This makes sense, as it is positive and not an unreasonable age. (An age of 612 years would be unreasonable!) We also note that 14 and 26 *do* add to 40, and that 26 *is* 12 more than 14.  ■

This is step 4.

## Further exercises

**Exercise 1.7**   Find the solution set of each of the following systems of simultaneous linear equations.

(a) $\begin{cases} x + 4y = -7 \\ 2x - y = 4 \\ -x + 2y = -5 \end{cases}$

(b) $\begin{cases} 4x - 6y = -2 \\ -6x + 9y = -3 \end{cases}$

(c) $\begin{cases} p + q + r = 5 \\ p + 2q + 3r = 11 \\ 3p + q + 4r = 13 \end{cases}$

**Exercise 1.8**   Find the points of intersection of the planes $x + y - z = 0$, $y - 2z = 0$ and $3x - y + 5z = 0$ in $\mathbb{R}^3$.

**Exercise 1.9**   Solve the following system of simultaneous linear equations in four unknowns.

$\begin{cases} a - b - 2c + d = 3 \\ \quad\;\; b + c + d = 3 \\ a - b - c + 2d = 7 \\ \quad\;\; b + c + 2d = 7 \end{cases}$

## 2   Row-reduction

After working through this section, you should be able to:

(a) write down the *augmented matrix* of a system of linear equations, and recover a system of linear equations from its augmented matrix;

(b) describe the three types of *elementary row operation*;

(c) recognise whether or not a given matrix is in *row-reduced form*;

(d) row-reduce a matrix;

(e) solve a system of linear equations by row-reducing its augmented matrix.

In this section we give a systematic method for solving a system of linear equations by Gauss–Jordan elimination. This method makes it easy to solve even quite large systems of linear equations. It involves a technique (row-reduction) that will be useful in another context later in this unit.

# 2.1  Augmented matrices

We begin by introducing an abbreviated notation for a system of linear equations.

You may have met the notion of a *matrix* at some point in your study of mathematics. A matrix is simply a rectangular array of objects, usually numbers, enclosed in brackets. Here are some examples:

$$\begin{pmatrix} 2 & -7 \\ -1 & \frac{1}{2} \\ 0 & 12 \end{pmatrix}, \quad \begin{pmatrix} 3.17 & 2.23 & 7.05 & 0.00 \\ 4.88 & 1.71 & 1.72 & 5.55 \end{pmatrix}, \quad \begin{pmatrix} 3 & 7 & 12 \\ -2 & 17 & 8 \\ 11 & 7 & -5 \end{pmatrix}.$$

In M208 we use round brackets for matrices; some texts use square ones.

The objects in a matrix are called its *entries*. The entries along a horizontal line form a *row*, and those down a vertical line form a *column*.

For example, the first row of the first matrix above is $2 \; -7$, and the second column of the same matrix is $\begin{matrix} -7 \\ \frac{1}{2} \\ 12 \end{matrix}$ .

We can abbreviate a system of linear equations by writing its coefficients and constants in the form of a matrix. For example, the system

$$\begin{cases} 4x + \; y = -7, \\ x - 3y = \; 0, \end{cases}$$

can be abbreviated as

$$\left( \begin{array}{cc|c} 4 & 1 & -7 \\ 1 & -3 & 0 \end{array} \right).$$

It is helpful to draw a vertical line separating the coefficients of the unknowns on the left-hand sides of the equations from the constants on the right-hand sides.

In general, the system

$$\begin{cases} a_{11}x_1 + \; a_{12}x_2 + \cdots + \; a_{1n}x_n = b_1, \\ a_{21}x_1 + \; a_{22}x_2 + \cdots + \; a_{2n}x_n = b_2, \\ \quad \vdots \qquad\quad \vdots \qquad\qquad\quad \vdots \qquad \vdots \\ a_{m1}x_1 + a_{m2}x_2 + \cdots + a_{mn}x_n = b_m, \end{cases}$$

of $m$ linear equations in $n$ unknowns $x_1, x_2, \ldots, x_n$ is abbreviated as the matrix

$$\left( \begin{array}{cccc|c} a_{11} & a_{12} & \cdots & a_{1n} & b_1 \\ a_{21} & a_{22} & \cdots & a_{2n} & b_2 \\ \vdots & \vdots & & \vdots & \vdots \\ a_{m1} & a_{m2} & \cdots & a_{mn} & b_m \end{array} \right).$$

This matrix is called the **augmented matrix** of the system. The word *augmented* reflects the fact that this is made up of a matrix formed by the coefficients of the unknowns on the left-hand sides of the equations, *augmented* by a matrix formed by the constants on the right-hand sides. Later, we shall sometimes consider these two matrices separately.

In the augmented matrix, each row corresponds to an equation, and each column (except the last) corresponds to an unknown, in the sense that it contains all the coefficients of that unknown from the various equations. The last column corresponds to the right-hand sides of the equations.

**Example 2.1**    Write down the augmented matrix of the following system of linear equations:

$$\begin{cases} x + 0y + 10z = \; 5, \\ 3x + \; y - \; 4z = -1, \\ 4x - 2y + \; 6z = \; 1. \end{cases}$$

Before writing down the augmented matrix of a system of linear equations, we must ensure that the unknowns appear in the same order in each equation, with gaps left for 'missing' unknowns (that is, unknowns whose coefficient is 0).

**Solution**   The augmented matrix of the system is

$$\left(\begin{array}{ccc|c} 1 & 0 & 10 & 5 \\ 3 & 1 & -4 & -1 \\ 4 & -2 & 6 & 1 \end{array}\right). \quad \blacksquare$$

**Example 2.2**   Write down the system of linear equations corresponding to the following augmented matrix, given that the unknowns are, in order, $x_1, x_2$:

$$\left(\begin{array}{cc|c} 1 & -2 & 5 \\ 0 & 1 & 9 \\ 4 & 3 & 0 \end{array}\right).$$

**Solution**   The corresponding system is

$$\begin{cases} x_1 - 2x_2 = 5, \\ \qquad\; x_2 = 9, \\ 4x_1 + 3x_2 = 0. \end{cases} \quad \blacksquare$$

**Exercise 2.1**

(a) Write down the augmented matrix of the following system of linear equations:

$$\begin{cases} 4x_1 - 2x_2 \qquad\quad = -7, \\ \qquad\; x_2 + 3x_3 = \;\; 0, \\ \qquad -3x_2 + \;\; x_3 = \;\; 3. \end{cases}$$

(b) Write down the system of linear equations corresponding to the following augmented matrix, given that the unknowns are, in order, $x, y, z, w$:

$$\left(\begin{array}{cccc|c} 2 & 3 & 0 & 7 & 1 \\ 0 & 1 & -7 & 0 & -1 \\ 1 & 0 & 3 & -1 & 2 \end{array}\right).$$

## 2.2  Elementary row operations

When we used Gauss–Jordan elimination to solve a system of linear equations in Section 1, we worked directly with the system itself; but it is often easier to apply the same method to its abbreviated form, the augmented matrix. The three elementary operations on the equations of the system correspond exactly to three equivalent operations on the rows of its augmented matrix.

Recall that the three elementary operations are as follows.    Subsection 1.3

1. Interchange two equations.
2. Multiply an equation by a non-zero number.
3. Change one equation by adding to it a multiple of another.

These correspond to the following operations on the rows of the augmented matrix.

1. Interchange two rows.
2. Multiply a row by a non-zero number.
3. Change one row by adding to it a multiple of another.

We call these **elementary row operations** of types 1, 2 and 3, respectively.

The next example shows a system of linear equations solved by Gauss–Jordan elimination. On the left, in Solution (a), we perform elementary operations on the system itself, as we did in Section 1. On the right, in Solution (b), we perform the corresponding elementary row operations on the augmented matrix of the system. You can see that in Solution (b), we have less to write down at each stage.

In this example, and elsewhere, we use the same notation for elementary row operations as we use for elementary operations ($\mathbf{r}_i \leftrightarrow \mathbf{r}_j$, and so on).

**Example 2.3**   Solve the following system of linear equations:

$$\begin{cases} x + y + 2z = 3, \\ 2x + 2y + 3z = 5, \\ x - y = 5. \end{cases}$$

This system is the one that we solved in Example 1.2; Solution (a) is simply repeated from there (in abbreviated form).

## Solution (a)

We perform a sequence of elementary operations on the system in order to transform it into a system with the same solution set but whose solution set is easy to write down.

$\begin{matrix} \mathbf{r}_1 \\ \mathbf{r}_2 \\ \mathbf{r}_3 \end{matrix}$ $\begin{cases} x + y + 2z = 3 \\ 2x + 2y + 3z = 5 \\ x - y = 5 \end{cases}$

$\begin{matrix} \\ \mathbf{r}_2 \to \mathbf{r}_2 - 2\mathbf{r}_1 \\ \mathbf{r}_3 \to \mathbf{r}_3 - \mathbf{r}_1 \end{matrix}$ $\begin{cases} x + y + 2z = 3 \\ -z = -1 \\ -2y - 2z = 2 \end{cases}$

$\begin{matrix} \\ \mathbf{r}_2 \leftrightarrow \mathbf{r}_3 \\ \end{matrix}$ $\begin{cases} x + y + 2z = 3 \\ -2y - 2z = 2 \\ -z = -1 \end{cases}$

$\begin{matrix} \\ \mathbf{r}_2 \to -\frac{1}{2}\mathbf{r}_2 \\ \end{matrix}$ $\begin{cases} x + y + 2z = 3 \\ y + z = -1 \\ -z = -1 \end{cases}$

$\mathbf{r}_1 \to \mathbf{r}_1 - \mathbf{r}_2$ $\begin{cases} x + z = 4 \\ y + z = -1 \\ -z = -1 \end{cases}$

$\begin{matrix} \\ \\ \mathbf{r}_3 \to -\mathbf{r}_3 \end{matrix}$ $\begin{cases} x + z = 4 \\ y + z = -1 \\ z = 1 \end{cases}$

$\begin{matrix} \mathbf{r}_1 \to \mathbf{r}_1 - \mathbf{r}_3 \\ \mathbf{r}_2 \to \mathbf{r}_2 - \mathbf{r}_3 \\ \end{matrix}$ $\begin{cases} x = 3 \\ y = -2 \\ z = 1 \end{cases}$

The solution is $x = 3$, $y = -2$, $z = 1$.

## Solution (b)

We perform a sequence of elementary row operations on the augmented matrix of the system in order to transform it into the augmented matrix of a system with the same solution set but whose solution set is easy to write down.

$\begin{matrix} \mathbf{r}_1 \\ \mathbf{r}_2 \\ \mathbf{r}_3 \end{matrix}$ $\left( \begin{array}{ccc|c} 1 & 1 & 2 & 3 \\ 2 & 2 & 3 & 5 \\ 1 & -1 & 0 & 5 \end{array} \right)$

$\begin{matrix} \\ \mathbf{r}_2 \to \mathbf{r}_2 - 2\mathbf{r}_1 \\ \mathbf{r}_3 \to \mathbf{r}_3 - \mathbf{r}_1 \end{matrix}$ $\left( \begin{array}{ccc|c} 1 & 1 & 2 & 3 \\ 0 & 0 & -1 & -1 \\ 0 & -2 & -2 & 2 \end{array} \right)$

$\begin{matrix} \\ \mathbf{r}_2 \leftrightarrow \mathbf{r}_3 \\ \end{matrix}$ $\left( \begin{array}{ccc|c} 1 & 1 & 2 & 3 \\ 0 & -2 & -2 & 2 \\ 0 & 0 & -1 & -1 \end{array} \right)$

$\begin{matrix} \\ \mathbf{r}_2 \to -\frac{1}{2}\mathbf{r}_2 \\ \end{matrix}$ $\left( \begin{array}{ccc|c} 1 & 1 & 2 & 3 \\ 0 & 1 & 1 & -1 \\ 0 & 0 & -1 & -1 \end{array} \right)$

$\mathbf{r}_1 \to \mathbf{r}_1 - \mathbf{r}_2$ $\left( \begin{array}{ccc|c} 1 & 0 & 1 & 4 \\ 0 & 1 & 1 & -1 \\ 0 & 0 & -1 & -1 \end{array} \right)$

$\begin{matrix} \\ \\ \mathbf{r}_3 \to -\mathbf{r}_3 \end{matrix}$ $\left( \begin{array}{ccc|c} 1 & 0 & 1 & 4 \\ 0 & 1 & 1 & -1 \\ 0 & 0 & 1 & 1 \end{array} \right)$

$\begin{matrix} \mathbf{r}_1 \to \mathbf{r}_1 - \mathbf{r}_3 \\ \mathbf{r}_2 \to \mathbf{r}_2 - \mathbf{r}_3 \\ \end{matrix}$ $\left( \begin{array}{ccc|c} 1 & 0 & 0 & 3 \\ 0 & 1 & 0 & -2 \\ 0 & 0 & 1 & 1 \end{array} \right)$

The corresponding system is

$$\begin{cases} x = 3, \\ y = -2, \\ z = 1. \end{cases}$$

The solution is $x = 3$, $y = -2$, $z = 1$.  ■

It is important to appreciate the following point about elementary row operations.

When a sequence of elementary row operations is performed on a matrix, each row operation in the sequence produces a new matrix, and the following row operation is then performed on that new matrix. For example, the working for the first two row operations in Solution (b) above should, strictly, be set out as follows.

$$
\begin{array}{c}
\mathbf{r}_1 \\
\mathbf{r}_2 \\
\mathbf{r}_3
\end{array}
\qquad
\left(
\begin{array}{ccc|c}
1 & 1 & 2 & 3 \\
2 & 2 & 3 & 5 \\
1 & -1 & 0 & 5
\end{array}
\right)
$$

$$
\mathbf{r}_2 \to \mathbf{r}_2 - 2\mathbf{r}_1
\qquad
\left(
\begin{array}{ccc|c}
1 & 1 & 2 & 3 \\
0 & 0 & -1 & -1 \\
1 & -1 & 0 & 5
\end{array}
\right)
$$

$$
\mathbf{r}_3 \to \mathbf{r}_3 - \mathbf{r}_1
\qquad
\left(
\begin{array}{ccc|c}
1 & 1 & 2 & 3 \\
0 & 0 & -1 & -1 \\
0 & -2 & -2 & 2
\end{array}
\right)
$$

However, we often perform two or more row operations in one step, to save time. Whenever we do this, we must ensure that when a row is changed by one of these row operations, the *new version* of that row is used when performing later row operations.

The easiest way to avoid difficulties is to perform two or more row operations in one step *only if none of these row operations changes a row that is then used by another of these row operations*. The above row operations $\mathbf{r}_2 \to \mathbf{r}_2 - 2\mathbf{r}_1$ and $\mathbf{r}_3 \to \mathbf{r}_3 - \mathbf{r}_1$ meet this criterion: the first changes only row 2, and the second does not involve row 2. In this course we perform two or more row operations in one step only if they meet this criterion.

## Row-sum check

We end this subsection by describing a simple checking method that can be useful for picking up arithmetical errors when we perform a sequence of elementary row operations on a matrix by hand.

To apply this method, we proceed as follows. To the right of each row of the initial matrix, we write down the sum of the entries in that row.

$$
\begin{array}{c}
\mathbf{r}_1 \\
\mathbf{r}_2 \\
\mathbf{r}_3
\end{array}
\qquad
\left(
\begin{array}{ccc|c}
1 & 1 & 2 & 3 \\
2 & 2 & 3 & 5 \\
1 & -1 & 0 & 5
\end{array}
\right)
\quad
\begin{array}{c}
7 \\
12 \\
5
\end{array}
$$

From then on, when performing elementary row operations, we treat this 'check column' of numbers as if it were an extra column of the matrix, and perform the row operations on it. So the first step of the calculation in Solution (b) above would look as follows.

$$
\begin{array}{c}
\mathbf{r}_2 \to \mathbf{r}_2 - 2\mathbf{r}_1 \\
\mathbf{r}_3 \to \mathbf{r}_3 - \mathbf{r}_1
\end{array}
\qquad
\left(
\begin{array}{ccc|c}
1 & 1 & 2 & 3 \\
0 & 0 & -1 & -1 \\
0 & -2 & -2 & 2
\end{array}
\right)
\quad
\begin{array}{c}
7 \\
-2 \\
-2
\end{array}
$$

At each step in the calculation, each entry in this extra column should still be the sum of the entries in the corresponding row. If this is not the case, an error has been made.

We have included the check column in an example in the audio frames.

## 2.3  Solving linear equations systematically

We now describe a systematic method for solving a system of linear equations by Gauss–Jordan elimination. The method involves performing elementary row operations on the augmented matrix of the system.

**Listen to the audio as you work through the frames.**

Audio

## 1. Example of a row-reduced matrix

## 2. General form of a row-reduced matrix

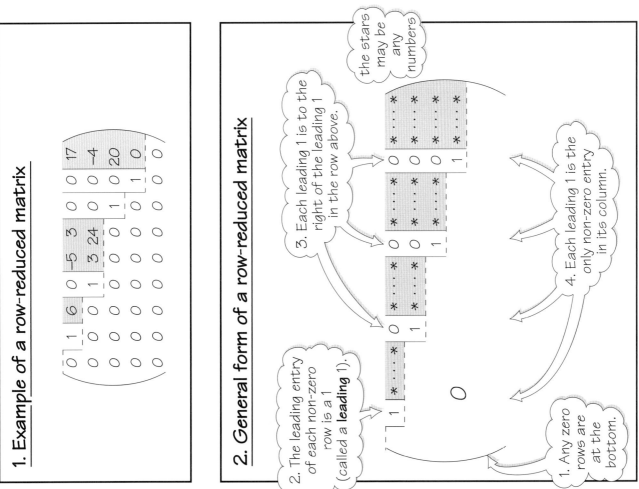

2. The leading entry of each non-zero row is a 1 (called a **leading** 1).

3. Each leading 1 is to the right of the leading 1 in the row above.

the stars may be any numbers

4. Each leading 1 is the only non-zero entry in its column.

1. Any zero rows are at the bottom.

## 3. More examples of row-reduced matrices

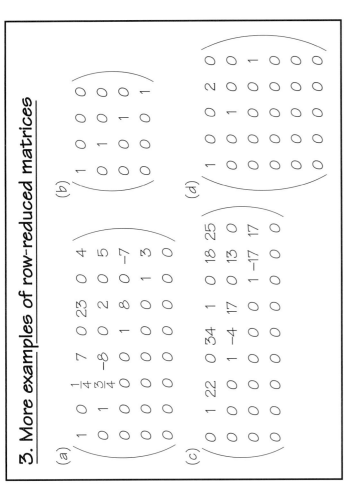

(a), (b), (c), (d)

## 4. Exercise 2.2

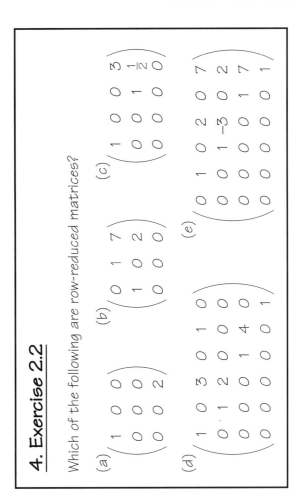

Which of the following are row-reduced matrices?

(a), (b), (c), (d), (e)

23

## 5. First example: solution from row-reduced form

$$\begin{pmatrix} 1 & 0 & 0 & | & 8 \\ 0 & 1 & 0 & | & 3 \\ 0 & 0 & 1 & | & -1 \end{pmatrix}$$

corresponds to

$$\begin{cases} x_1 \qquad\quad = 8, \\ \quad x_2 \qquad = 3, \\ \qquad x_3 = -1. \end{cases}$$

*(unique solution)*

The solution is
$x_1 = 8$, $x_2 = 3$, $x_3 = -1$.

## 6. Second example

$$\begin{pmatrix} 1 & 0 & 6 & | & 7 \\ 0 & 1 & -4 & | & 2 \end{pmatrix}$$

corresponds to

$$\begin{cases} x_1 \quad + 6x_3 = 7, \\ \quad x_2 - 4x_3 = 2, \end{cases}$$

so
$$\begin{cases} x_1 = 7 - 6x_3, \\ x_2 = 2 + 4x_3. \end{cases}$$

*($x_1$ and $x_2$ are **leading** unknowns)*

*($x_3$ is a **non-leading** unknown — set $x_3 = k$ ($k \in \mathbb{R}$))*

The general solution is
$$x_1 = 7 - 6k,$$
$$x_2 = 2 + 4k,$$
$$x_3 = k.$$

*(all the unknowns are expressed in terms of the **parameter** k)*

*(infinitely many solutions)*

## 7. Third example

$$\begin{pmatrix} 1 & -6 & 0 & | & 0 \\ 0 & 0 & 1 & | & 0 \\ 0 & 0 & 0 & | & 1 \end{pmatrix}$$

corresponds to

$$\begin{cases} x_1 - 6x_2 \qquad = 0, \\ \qquad\quad x_3 = 0, \\ \qquad\quad\; 0 = 1. \end{cases}$$

*(no solution)*

Original system of equations is inconsistent.

## 8. Fourth example

$$\begin{pmatrix} 1 & 0 & 2 & 0 & 5 & | & 4 \\ 0 & 1 & -3 & 0 & -1 & | & 2 \\ 0 & 0 & 0 & 1 & 3 & | & -7 \\ 0 & 0 & 0 & 0 & 0 & | & 0 \end{pmatrix}$$

corresponds to

$$\begin{cases} x_1 \quad\; + 2x_3 \qquad + 5x_5 = 4, \\ \quad x_2 - 3x_3 \qquad - x_5 = 2, \\ \qquad\qquad\quad x_4 + 3x_5 = -7, \end{cases}$$

so
$$\begin{cases} x_1 = 4 - 2x_3 - 5x_5, \\ x_2 = 2 + 3x_3 + x_5, \\ x_4 = -7 \qquad - 3x_5. \end{cases}$$

*($x_1, x_2, x_4$ are leading unknowns)*

*($x_3, x_5$ are non-leading unknowns — set $x_3 = k$, $x_5 = l$ ($k, l \in \mathbb{R}$))*

The general solution is
$$x_1 = 4 - 2k - 5l,$$
$$x_2 = 2 + 3k + l,$$
$$x_3 = k,$$
$$x_4 = -7 - 3l,$$
$$x_5 = l.$$

*(all the unknowns are expressed in terms of the parameters k, l)*

*(infinitely many solutions)*

## 9. Exercise 2.3

Solve the system corresponding to each of the following row-reduced matrices.

(a) Assume that the unknowns are $x_1$, $x_2$.

$$\begin{pmatrix} 1 & 0 & \left| \frac{1}{3} \right. \\ 0 & 1 & \left| \frac{2}{3} \right. \end{pmatrix}$$

(b) Assume that the unknowns are $x_1$, $x_2$, $x_3$.

$$\begin{pmatrix} 1 & 0 & 6 & | & 0 \\ 0 & 1 & 7 & | & 0 \\ 0 & 0 & 0 & | & 1 \end{pmatrix}$$

(c) Assume that the unknowns are $x_1$, $x_2$, $x_3$, $x_4$, $x_5$.

$$\begin{pmatrix} 1 & 3 & 0 & 2 & 0 & | & -7 \\ 0 & 0 & 1 & -3 & 0 & | & 8 \\ 0 & 0 & 0 & 0 & 1 & | & 11 \\ 0 & 0 & 0 & 0 & 0 & | & 0 \end{pmatrix}$$

(d) Assume that the unknowns are $x_1$, $x_2$, $x_3$, $x_4$.

$$\begin{pmatrix} 1 & 0 & 0 & 1 & | & 0 \\ 0 & 1 & 0 & 4 & | & 3 \\ 0 & 0 & 1 & 0 & | & 0 \end{pmatrix}$$

## 10. Strategy 2.1   Row-reducing a matrix

Carry out the following four steps, first with row 1 as the current row, then with row 2, and so on, until

EITHER    every row has been the current row,

OR         Step 1 is not possible.

*Step 1:
select the column for the current row's leading 1*

### Step 1

Select the first column from the left that has at least one non-zero entry in or below the current row.

*Steps 2 and 3:
create a leading 1*

### Step 2

If the current row has a 0 in the selected column, interchange it with a row below which has a non-zero entry in that column.

### Step 3

If the entry now in the current row and the selected column is c, multiply the current row by 1/c to create a leading 1.

*Step 4:
make each entry above and below the leading 1 into a 0*

### Step 4

Add suitable multiples of the current row to the other rows to make each entry above and below the leading 1 into a 0.

25

## 11. Example: row 1 is the current row

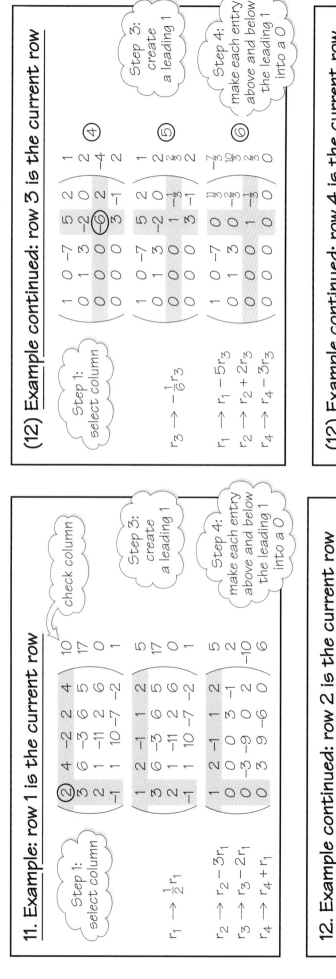

Step 1:
select column

$$r_1 \rightarrow \tfrac{1}{2}r_1$$

check column

Step 3:
create
a leading 1

$$r_2 \rightarrow r_2 - 3r_1$$
$$r_3 \rightarrow r_3 - 2r_1$$
$$r_4 \rightarrow r_4 + r_1$$

Step 4:
make each entry
above and below
the leading 1
into a 0

## 12. Example continued: row 2 is the current row

Step 1:
select column

$$r_2 \leftrightarrow r_4$$

Steps 2 and 3:
create
a leading 1

$$r_2 \rightarrow \tfrac{1}{3}r_2$$

$$r_1 \rightarrow r_1 - 2r_2$$
$$r_3 \rightarrow r_3 + 3r_2$$

Step 4:
make each entry
above and below
the leading 1
into a 0

## (12) Example continued: row 3 is the current row

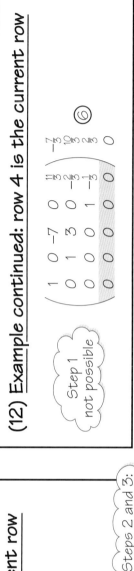

Step 1:
select column

Step 3:
create
a leading 1

$$r_3 \rightarrow -\tfrac{1}{6}r_3$$

Step 4:
make each entry
above and below
the leading 1
into a 0

$$r_1 \rightarrow r_1 - 5r_3$$
$$r_2 \rightarrow r_2 + 2r_3$$
$$r_4 \rightarrow r_4 - 3r_3$$

## (12) Example continued: row 4 is the current row

Step 1
not possible

## 13. Exercise 2.4

Row-reduce the following matrices.

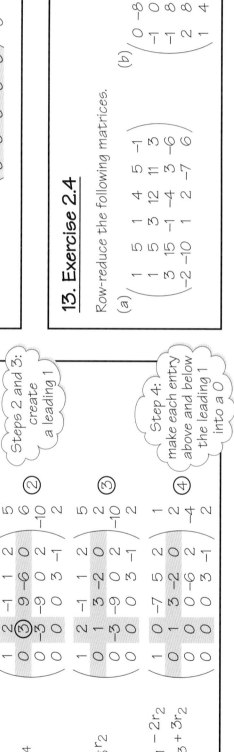

(a) $\begin{pmatrix} 1 & 5 & 1 & 4 & 5 & -1 \\ 1 & 5 & 3 & 12 & 11 & 3 \\ 3 & 15 & -1 & -4 & 3 & -6 \\ -2 & -10 & 1 & 2 & -7 & 6 \end{pmatrix}$

(b) $\begin{pmatrix} 0 & -8 & 8 & -14 \\ -1 & 0 & -4 & -6 \\ -1 & 8 & -12 & 8 \\ 2 & 8 & 0 & 24 \\ 1 & 4 & 0 & 14 \end{pmatrix}$

26

## 16. Theorem 2.1

Every matrix has a unique row-reduced form.

*(proof omitted)*

## 17. Strategy 2.2   To solve a system of linear equations

given a system of linear equations

$\downarrow$

form the augmented matrix

$\uparrow$ *(reduce using elementary row operations)*

obtain the row-reduced matrix

$\downarrow$

solve the simplified system of linear equations

$\downarrow$

solution

## 18. Exercise 2.5

Use Strategy 2.2 in Frame 17 to solve the following systems of linear equations.

(a) $\begin{cases} 3x + 5y - 12z = 4 \\ x + y = 2 \\ 2x + 3y - 4z = 5 \end{cases}$

(b) $\begin{cases} x_1 - 4x_2 - 4x_3 + 3x_4 + 6x_5 = 2 \\ 2x_1 - 5x_2 - 6x_3 + 6x_4 + 9x_5 = 3 \\ 2x_1 + 4x_2 \qquad\;\; + 9x_4 + 2x_5 = 0 \end{cases}$

## 14. Modifying the method

*Step 1: select column*

$\begin{pmatrix} 1 & 3 & \textcircled{4} & 2 & 7 \\ 0 & 4 & 5 & 7 & 16 \\ 0 & 3 & 4 & 9 & 16 \end{pmatrix}$ ①

*(row 2 is the current row)*

*The official Step 3 would give fractions:*

$r_2 \to \tfrac{1}{4} r_2$

$\begin{pmatrix} 1 & 3 & 1 & 2 & 7 \\ 0 & 1 & \frac{5}{4} & \frac{7}{4} & 4 \\ 0 & 3 & 4 & 9 & 16 \end{pmatrix}$

Instead, try

$r_2 \to r_2 - r_3$

$\begin{pmatrix} 1 & 3 & 1 & 2 & 7 \\ 0 & 1 & 1 & -2 & 0 \\ 0 & 3 & 4 & 9 & 16 \end{pmatrix}$ ②

$r_1 \to r_1 - 3r_2$
$r_3 \to r_3 - 3r_2$

$\begin{pmatrix} 1 & 0 & -2 & 8 & 7 \\ 0 & 1 & 1 & -2 & 0 \\ 0 & 0 & 1 & 15 & 16 \end{pmatrix}$ ③

*(the unofficial Step 3: create a leading 1)*

*(Step 4)*

## 15. A warning

$\begin{pmatrix} 1 & 3 & 1 & 2 & 7 \\ 0 & 4 & 5 & 7 & 16 \\ 0 & 3 & 4 & 9 & 16 \end{pmatrix}$

*(row 2 is the current row)*

Instead of $r_2 \to \tfrac{1}{4} r_2$, try

$r_2 \to r_2 - r_1$

$\begin{pmatrix} 1 & 3 & 1 & 2 & 7 \\ -1 & 1 & 4 & 5 & 9 \\ 0 & 3 & 4 & 9 & 16 \end{pmatrix}$

*(not helpful...)*

*(in modifications, don't use rows above current row)*

*(...this is not a leading 1)*

# Further exercises

**Exercise 2.6**   Which of the following are row-reduced matrices?

(a) $\begin{pmatrix} 0 & 0 & 1 & 5 \\ 1 & 0 & 0 & 7 \\ 0 & 1 & 0 & 7 \end{pmatrix}$
(b) $\begin{pmatrix} 1 & 14 & 0 & 23 \\ 0 & 0 & 1 & 44 \\ 0 & 0 & 0 & 0 \end{pmatrix}$

(c) $\begin{pmatrix} 1 & 0 & 0 & 0 & 0 & 1 \\ 0 & 0 & 1 & 0 & 0 & 0 \\ 0 & 0 & 0 & 0 & 1 & 0 \\ 0 & 0 & 0 & 0 & 0 & 0 \\ 0 & 0 & 0 & 0 & 0 & 0 \end{pmatrix}$
(d) $\begin{pmatrix} 0 & 1 & 0 & -3 & 12 \\ 0 & 0 & 1 & 0 & 7 \\ 0 & 0 & 0 & 1 & 2 \\ 0 & 0 & 0 & 0 & 0 \\ 0 & 0 & 0 & 0 & 0 \end{pmatrix}$

(e) $\begin{pmatrix} 0 & 1 & \frac{1}{7} & 0 & -6 & 24 & -\frac{3}{7} \\ 0 & 0 & 0 & 1 & 3 & -\frac{2}{7} & \frac{1}{7} \end{pmatrix}$
(f) $\begin{pmatrix} 0 & 0 & 0 & 0 \\ 0 & 0 & 0 & 0 \end{pmatrix}$

**Exercise 2.7**   Solve the systems of linear equations corresponding to the following row-reduced augmented matrices. (Assume that the unknowns are $x_1, x_2, \ldots$)

(a) $\left( \begin{array}{ccc|c} 1 & 0 & 0 & 7 \\ 0 & 1 & 0 & -6 \\ 0 & 0 & 1 & 5 \end{array} \right)$

(b) $\left( \begin{array}{ccc|c} 1 & \frac{1}{7} & 0 & 1 \\ 0 & 0 & 1 & 3 \\ 0 & 0 & 0 & 0 \end{array} \right)$

(c) $\left( \begin{array}{cccc|c} 1 & 0 & 4 & 0 & 0 \\ 0 & 1 & -3 & 0 & 0 \\ 0 & 0 & 0 & 1 & 0 \end{array} \right)$

(d) $\left( \begin{array}{ccccc|c} 1 & 3 & 0 & -2 & 0 & 0 \\ 0 & 0 & 1 & 2 & 1 & 0 \\ 0 & 0 & 0 & 0 & 0 & 1 \end{array} \right)$

(e) $\left( \begin{array}{cccc|c} 1 & 0 & -5 & 0 & 4 \\ 0 & 1 & -7 & 3 & 12 \\ 0 & 0 & 0 & 0 & 0 \\ 0 & 0 & 0 & 0 & 0 \end{array} \right)$

**Exercise 2.8**   Solve each of the following systems of linear equations by reducing its augmented matrix to row-reduced form.

(a) $\begin{cases} 3x - 11y - 3z = 3 \\ 2x - 6y - 2z = 1 \\ 5x - 17y - 6z = 2 \\ 4x - 8y = 7 \end{cases}$

(b) $\begin{cases} a - 4c - 2d = -1 \\ a + 2b - 2c + 4d = 6 \\ 2a + 4b - 3c + 9d = 9 \\ 2a + b - 5c + d = -4 \end{cases}$

(c) $\begin{cases} 2x_1 + 2x_2 - 5x_3 + 6x_4 + 10x_5 = -2 \\ 2x_1 + 2x_2 - 6x_3 + 6x_4 + 8x_5 = 0 \\ 2x_1 - x_3 + 2x_4 + 7x_5 = 7 \\ x_1 + 2x_2 - 5x_3 + 5x_4 + 4x_5 = -3 \end{cases}$

# 3    Matrix algebra

After working through this section, you should be able to:

(a) perform the matrix operations of addition, multiplication and transposition;

(b) recognise the following types of matrix: *square, zero, diagonal, lower-triangular, upper-triangular, identity, symmetric*;

(c) express a system of simultaneous linear equations in *matrix form*.

Earlier, we saw how an augmented matrix concisely represents a system of simultaneous linear equations.

Subsection 2.1

A matrix of *size* $m \times n$ has $m$ rows and $n$ columns. An $n \times n$ matrix is called a *square* matrix. The entry in the $i$th row and $j$th column of a matrix $\mathbf{A}$ is called the $(i, j)$-entry, often denoted by $a_{ij}$. In general, we write $\mathbf{A}$ or $(a_{ij})$ to denote a matrix:

$$\mathbf{A} = \begin{pmatrix} a_{11} & a_{12} & \cdots & a_{1n} \\ a_{21} & a_{22} & \cdots & a_{2n} \\ \vdots & \vdots & & \vdots \\ a_{m1} & a_{m2} & \cdots & a_{mn} \end{pmatrix} = (a_{ij}).$$

**Exercise 3.1**    Write down the size of each of the following matrices. Which matrices are square? What is the $(2, 3)$-entry in each matrix?

(a) $\begin{pmatrix} 3 & -4 & 2 & 6 \\ -1 & 0 & 5 & 1 \end{pmatrix}$    (b) $\begin{pmatrix} 1 & 3 & 7 \\ -1 & 10 & 0 \\ 2 & 4 & 1 \end{pmatrix}$    (c) $\begin{pmatrix} 2 & 1 \\ -3 & 7 \end{pmatrix}$

Two $m \times n$ matrices $\mathbf{A} = (a_{ij})$ and $\mathbf{B} = (b_{ij})$ are *equal* if $a_{ij} = b_{ij}$ for all values of $i$ and $j$.

---

**Definition**    Two matrices $\mathbf{A}$ and $\mathbf{B}$ of the same size are **equal** if all their corresponding entries agree. We write $\mathbf{A} = \mathbf{B}$.

---

Thus $\begin{pmatrix} 1 & 2 & 3 \\ 4 & 5 & 6 \end{pmatrix}$ is not equal to $\begin{pmatrix} 1 & 2 & 1 \\ 4 & 5 & 6 \end{pmatrix}$ as the $(1, 3)$-entries differ,

and $\begin{pmatrix} 1 & 1 & 1 \\ 1 & 1 & 1 \end{pmatrix}$ is not equal to $\begin{pmatrix} 1 & 1 \\ 1 & 1 \\ 1 & 1 \end{pmatrix}$ as the matrices are different

sizes. A matrix of size $1 \times 1$ comprises just a single entry; we often omit the brackets and identify such matrices with ordinary numbers—*scalars*; for example, we identify the matrix $(5)$ with the number 5.

We call a matrix with just one column a *column matrix*, and a matrix with just one row a *row matrix*. For example,

$\begin{pmatrix} 1 \\ 2 \\ 3 \end{pmatrix}$ is a column matrix    and    $\begin{pmatrix} 1 & 2 & 3 & 4 \end{pmatrix}$ is a row matrix.

# 3.1 Matrix addition

Let $\mathbf{a} = (a_1, a_2)$ and $\mathbf{b} = (b_1, b_2)$ be two vectors in $\mathbb{R}^2$. Their *sum* is defined    Unit LA1, Subsection 2.2.
to be the vector

$$\mathbf{a} + \mathbf{b} = (a_1 + b_1, a_2 + b_2).$$

For example,

$$(1, 2) + (-2, 3) = (1 + (-2), 2 + 3) = (-1, 5).$$

We add matrices in precisely the same way; that is, by adding
corresponding entries. For example,

$$\begin{pmatrix} 1 & 0 \\ 1 & 2 \end{pmatrix} + \begin{pmatrix} 2 & -1 \\ 0 & 1 \end{pmatrix} = \begin{pmatrix} 1+2 & 0+(-1) \\ 1+0 & 2+1 \end{pmatrix} = \begin{pmatrix} 3 & -1 \\ 1 & 3 \end{pmatrix}$$

and

$$\begin{pmatrix} 2 & 1 & 5 \\ 3 & 0 & 1 \end{pmatrix} + \begin{pmatrix} -2 & 4 & 2 \\ 1 & 3 & 2 \end{pmatrix} = \begin{pmatrix} 0 & 5 & 7 \\ 4 & 3 & 3 \end{pmatrix}.$$

It is clear that only matrices of the same size can be added together. For
example, the following is meaningless:

$$\begin{pmatrix} 1 & 2 & 3 \\ 4 & 5 & 6 \end{pmatrix} + \begin{pmatrix} 1 & 2 \\ 3 & 4 \\ 5 & 6 \end{pmatrix}.$$

We now write down a general formula for the addition of two matrices.

---

**Definition**   The **sum** of two $m \times n$ matrices $\mathbf{A} = (a_{ij})$ and $\mathbf{B} = (b_{ij})$
is the $m \times n$ matrix $\mathbf{A} + \mathbf{B} = (a_{ij} + b_{ij})$ given by

$$\mathbf{A} + \mathbf{B} = \begin{pmatrix} a_{11} + b_{11} & a_{12} + b_{12} & \cdots & a_{1n} + b_{1n} \\ a_{21} + b_{21} & a_{22} + b_{22} & \cdots & a_{2n} + b_{2n} \\ \vdots & \vdots & & \vdots \\ a_{m1} + b_{m1} & a_{m2} + b_{m2} & \cdots & a_{mn} + b_{mn} \end{pmatrix}.$$

---

**Exercise 3.2**   Evaluate the following matrix sums, where possible.

(a) $\begin{pmatrix} 1 & -3 \\ -2 & 54 \end{pmatrix} + \begin{pmatrix} 2 & 0 \\ 4 & 1 \end{pmatrix}$      (b) $\begin{pmatrix} 2 & 0 \\ 4 & 1 \end{pmatrix} + \begin{pmatrix} 1 & -3 \\ -2 & 54 \end{pmatrix}$

(c) $\begin{pmatrix} 1 & 2 \\ 1 & 0 \\ 4 & 1 \end{pmatrix} + \begin{pmatrix} 1 & 2 & 2 \\ 1 & 3 & 1 \\ -2 & 4 & 5 \end{pmatrix}$      (d) $\begin{pmatrix} 0 & 6 & -2 \\ 1 & 8 & 2 \\ 0 & 3 & 4 \end{pmatrix} + \begin{pmatrix} 1 & 2 & 9 \\ 1 & 0 & 4 \\ 3 & -4 & 1 \end{pmatrix}$

In Exercise 3.2, parts (a) and (b) give the same answer. The commutative
law, $a + b = b + a$, holds for the addition of scalars, as does the associative
law, $a + (b + c) = (a + b) + c$, for all $a, b, c \in \mathbb{R}$. Since matrix addition is
defined in terms of addition of scalars, matrix addition is both
commutative and associative.

---

**Theorem 3.1**   For all matrices $\mathbf{A}$, $\mathbf{B}$ and $\mathbf{C}$ of the same size,

$$\mathbf{A} + \mathbf{B} = \mathbf{B} + \mathbf{A} \quad \text{(commutative law)},$$

$$\mathbf{A} + (\mathbf{B} + \mathbf{C}) = (\mathbf{A} + \mathbf{B}) + \mathbf{C} \quad \text{(associative law)}.$$

---

**Proof**    Let $\mathbf{A} = (a_{ij})$ and $\mathbf{B} = (b_{ij})$. To prove the commutative law, we add the corresponding entries of these two matrices.

The $(i, j)$-entry of the matrix $\mathbf{A} + \mathbf{B}$ is $a_{ij} + b_{ij}$, and that of $\mathbf{B} + \mathbf{A}$ is $b_{ij} + a_{ij}$.

Since $a_{ij}$ and $b_{ij}$ are scalars, $a_{ij} + b_{ij} = b_{ij} + a_{ij}$. Thus

$$\mathbf{A} + \mathbf{B} = (a_{ij} + b_{ij}) = (b_{ij} + a_{ij}) = \mathbf{B} + \mathbf{A}.$$

We ask you to prove the associative law in Exercise 3.3.  ∎

**Exercise 3.3**    Prove the associative law: for all matrices $\mathbf{A}$, $\mathbf{B}$ and $\mathbf{C}$ of the same size,
$$\mathbf{A} + (\mathbf{B} + \mathbf{C}) = (\mathbf{A} + \mathbf{B}) + \mathbf{C}.$$

## Zero matrix

We have seen that matrices can be added in a way analogous to addition of scalars. There is a type of matrix that corresponds to the number 0, namely, the *zero matrix*, which, as its name suggests, is a matrix of 0s. It is denoted by $\mathbf{0}_{m,n}$, or by $\mathbf{0}$ when it is clear from the context which size of matrix is intended.

---

**Definition**    The $m \times n$ **zero matrix** $\mathbf{0}_{m,n}$ is the $m \times n$ matrix in which all entries are 0.

---

The following are all examples of zero matrices:

$$\begin{pmatrix} 0 \\ 0 \end{pmatrix}, \quad \begin{pmatrix} 0 & 0 & 0 \end{pmatrix}, \quad \begin{pmatrix} 0 & 0 & 0 & 0 \\ 0 & 0 & 0 & 0 \\ 0 & 0 & 0 & 0 \end{pmatrix} \quad \text{and} \quad \begin{pmatrix} 0 & 0 & \cdots & 0 \\ 0 & 0 & \cdots & 0 \\ \vdots & \vdots & & \vdots \\ 0 & 0 & \cdots & 0 \end{pmatrix}.$$

The following exercise shows that the zero matrix acts in the same way as the number 0 under the operation of addition. The zero matrix is the *identity* element for the operation of matrix addition.

**Exercise 3.4**    Show that $\mathbf{A} + \mathbf{0} = \mathbf{A}$ for any matrix $\mathbf{A} = (a_{ij})$.

---

**Definition**    The **negative** of an $m \times n$ matrix $\mathbf{A} = (a_{ij})$ is the $m \times n$ matrix
$$-\mathbf{A} = (-a_{ij}).$$

---

For example, if
$$\mathbf{A} = \begin{pmatrix} 1 & -2 & 3 \\ -4 & 5 & -6 \end{pmatrix},$$
then
$$-\mathbf{A} = \begin{pmatrix} -1 & 2 & -3 \\ 4 & -5 & 6 \end{pmatrix}.$$

The negative of a matrix acts in the same way as the negative of a number under the operation of addition.

---

**Theorem 3.2**   Let $\mathbf{A}$ be a matrix. Then

$$\mathbf{A} + (-\mathbf{A}) = (-\mathbf{A}) + \mathbf{A} = \mathbf{0}.$$

---

**Proof**   Let $\mathbf{A} = (a_{ij})$, so $-\mathbf{A} = (-a_{ij})$. We add corresponding entries: the $(i,j)$-entry of the matrix $\mathbf{A} + (-\mathbf{A})$ is $a_{ij} + (-a_{ij}) = 0$. Thus the matrix $\mathbf{A} + (-\mathbf{A})$ is the zero matrix $\mathbf{0}$.

Matrix addition is commutative, so $(-\mathbf{A}) + \mathbf{A} = \mathbf{A} + (-\mathbf{A})$. Thus $(-\mathbf{A}) + \mathbf{A}$ is also the zero matrix $\mathbf{0}$.   ∎

The $m \times n$ matrix $-\mathbf{A}$ is the *additive inverse* of the $m \times n$ matrix $\mathbf{A}$. Since the four group axioms

G1 CLOSURE,   G2 IDENTITY,   G3 INVERSES,   G4 ASSOCIATIVITY

are satisfied, the set of $m \times n$ matrices under the operation of matrix addition forms a *group*.

The group axioms were defined in Unit GTA1.

Using the negative of a matrix, we can *subtract* matrices:

$$\mathbf{A} - \mathbf{B} = \mathbf{A} + (-\mathbf{B}).$$

**Exercise 3.5**   Evaluate the following matrix differences, where possible.

(a) $\begin{pmatrix} 3 & 0 \\ 2 & 7 \end{pmatrix} - \begin{pmatrix} 10 & 3 \\ 1 & 5 \\ 15 & 12 \end{pmatrix}$   (b) $\begin{pmatrix} 5 & 8 & 12 \\ 7 & 2 & -1 \end{pmatrix} - \begin{pmatrix} 3 & 10 & 2 \\ 4 & 9 & 21 \end{pmatrix}$

## 3.2 Multiplication of a matrix by a scalar

Multiplication of a vector by a scalar generalises in the obvious way to matrices. To multiply the vector $\mathbf{a} = (a_1, a_2)$ by the scalar $k$, we multiply each entry in turn by $k$; this gives

Unit LA1, Subsection 2.2.

$$k\mathbf{a} = (ka_1, ka_2).$$

Similarly, to multiply a matrix by a scalar $k$, we multiply each entry by $k$. For example,

$$3\begin{pmatrix} 1 & 2 & 3 \\ 4 & 5 & 6 \end{pmatrix} = \begin{pmatrix} 3 & 6 & 9 \\ 12 & 15 & 18 \end{pmatrix}, \quad -\tfrac{1}{2}\begin{pmatrix} -4 & 2 \\ 0 & -6 \end{pmatrix} = \begin{pmatrix} 2 & -1 \\ 0 & 3 \end{pmatrix}.$$

---

**Definition**   The **scalar multiple** of an $m \times n$ matrix $\mathbf{A} = (a_{ij})$ by a scalar $k$ is the $m \times n$ matrix

$$k\mathbf{A} = \begin{pmatrix} ka_{11} & ka_{12} & \cdots & ka_{1n} \\ ka_{21} & ka_{22} & \cdots & ka_{2n} \\ \vdots & \vdots & & \vdots \\ ka_{m1} & ka_{m2} & \cdots & ka_{mn} \end{pmatrix} = (ka_{ij}).$$

---

Notice that $(-1)\mathbf{A} = -\mathbf{A}$ and $0\mathbf{A} = \mathbf{0}$.

**Exercise 3.6**   Let

$$\mathbf{A} = \begin{pmatrix} 5 & -3 \\ 2 & 3 \\ -1 & 0 \end{pmatrix} \quad \text{and} \quad \mathbf{B} = \begin{pmatrix} 2 & 1 \\ -2 & -7 \\ 3 & 5 \end{pmatrix}.$$

Evaluate the following.

(a) $4\mathbf{A}$     (b) $4\mathbf{B}$     (c) $4\mathbf{A} + 4\mathbf{B}$     (d) $4(\mathbf{A} + \mathbf{B})$

You should have obtained the same answer for parts (c) and (d) of Exercise 3.6. In fact, we have the following general result.

---

**Theorem 3.3**   For all matrices $\mathbf{A}$ and $\mathbf{B}$ of the same size, and all scalars $k$, the distributive law holds; that is,

$$k(\mathbf{A} + \mathbf{B}) = k\mathbf{A} + k\mathbf{B}.$$

You are asked to prove Theorem 3.3 in Exercise 3.16.

---

## 3.3  Matrix multiplication

You have seen that the addition of matrices generalises the addition of scalars and of vectors. In Unit LA1, Subsection 3.1, we introduced a method of 'multiplying' vectors—the *dot product*. Let $\mathbf{a} = (a_1, a_2, a_3)$ and $\mathbf{b} = (b_1, b_2, b_3)$ be two vectors in $\mathbb{R}^3$. Then

$$\mathbf{a} \cdot \mathbf{b} = a_1 b_1 + a_2 b_2 + a_3 b_3.$$

Matrix multiplication is a generalisation of this idea.

To form the product of two matrices $\mathbf{A}$ and $\mathbf{B}$, we combine the rows of $\mathbf{A}$ with the columns of $\mathbf{B}$. The $(i, j)$-entry of the product $\mathbf{AB}$ is obtained by multiplying the entries in the $i$th row of $\mathbf{A}$ with the corresponding entries in the $j$th column of $\mathbf{B}$, and summing the products obtained.

For example, let

$$\mathbf{A} = \begin{pmatrix} 1 & 2 & 3 \\ 4 & 5 & 6 \end{pmatrix} \quad \text{and} \quad \mathbf{B} = \begin{pmatrix} 1 & 2 & 3 \\ 4 & 5 & 6 \\ 7 & 8 & 9 \end{pmatrix}.$$

To obtain the $(1, 2)$-entry of the product $\mathbf{AB}$, we combine the *first* row of $\mathbf{A}$ with the *second* column of $\mathbf{B}$: we multiply together the first entry of the first row of $\mathbf{A}$ and the first entry of the second column of $\mathbf{B}$, then multiply together the second entries of each, and then the third entries, finally adding these three numbers. The $(1, 2)$-entry of $\mathbf{AB}$ is thus

$$(1 \times 2) + (2 \times 5) + (3 \times 8) = 2 + 10 + 24 = 36.$$

To obtain the $(2, 3)$-entry of the product $\mathbf{AB}$, we combine the *second* row of $\mathbf{A}$ with the *third* column of $\mathbf{B}$. The $(2, 3)$-entry of $\mathbf{AB}$ is

$$(4 \times 3) + (5 \times 6) + (6 \times 9) = 12 + 30 + 54 = 96.$$

We can compare the way in which we combined the first row of $\mathbf{A}$ and the second column of $\mathbf{B}$ with the dot product of two vectors:

$$(1, 2, 3) \cdot (2, 5, 8) = (1 \times 2) + (2 \times 5) + (3 \times 8) = 36.$$

We therefore say that we take the *dot product* of the first row of $\mathbf{A}$ with the second column of $\mathbf{B}$ to obtain the $(1, 2)$-entry of the product $\mathbf{AB}$.

Subsection 3.1

One way to remember how to multiply matrices $\mathbf{A}$ and $\mathbf{B}$ is to picture running along the rows of $\mathbf{A}$ and then diving down the columns of $\mathbf{B}$.

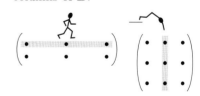

Likewise, we take the dot product of the second row of $\mathbf{A}$ with the third column of $\mathbf{B}$ to obtain the $(2,3)$-entry of the product $\mathbf{AB}$:

$$(4,5,6) \cdot (3,6,9) = (4 \times 3) + (5 \times 6) + (6 \times 9) = 96.$$

**Exercise 3.7**  Find the $(2,1)$-entry of the product $\mathbf{AB}$, for the matrices $\mathbf{A}$ and $\mathbf{B}$ given above.

To form the matrix product $\mathbf{AB}$, we combine each row of $\mathbf{A}$ with each column of $\mathbf{B}$. We therefore obtain $2 \times 3$ entries in the product $\mathbf{AB}$, so this matrix has 2 rows and 3 columns. We have found three of the six entries, as highlighted below.

$$\begin{pmatrix} 1 & 2 & 3 \\ 4 & 5 & 6 \end{pmatrix} \begin{pmatrix} 1 & 2 & 3 \\ 4 & 5 & 6 \\ 7 & 8 & 9 \end{pmatrix} = \begin{pmatrix} 30 & 36 & 42 \\ 66 & 81 & 96 \end{pmatrix}$$

You should check the other entries.

Notice that we *can* form the product $\mathbf{AB}$ since the matrix $\mathbf{A}$ has the same number of entries in a row as the matrix $\mathbf{B}$ has in a column; that is, the number of columns of $\mathbf{A}$ is equal to the number of rows of $\mathbf{B}$.

The product $\mathbf{AB}$ is not defined when the number of columns of the matrix $\mathbf{A}$ is not equal to the number of rows of the matrix $\mathbf{B}$.

---

**Definition**  The **product** of an $m \times n$ matrix $\mathbf{A}$ with an $n \times p$ matrix $\mathbf{B}$ is the $m \times p$ matrix $\mathbf{AB}$ whose $(i,j)$-entry is the dot product of the $i$th row of $\mathbf{A}$ with the $j$th column of $\mathbf{B}$.

---

Notice that the product $\mathbf{AB}$ has the same number of rows as the matrix $\mathbf{A}$, and the same number of columns as the matrix $\mathbf{B}$.

Schematically,

Example 3.1  Evaluate (where possible) the matrix products $\mathbf{AB}$, where:

(a)  $\mathbf{A} = \begin{pmatrix} 2 & 1 \\ -3 & 0 \end{pmatrix}$ and $\mathbf{B} = \begin{pmatrix} 3 & -2 & 0 \\ 1 & 1 & 4 \end{pmatrix}$;

(b)  $\mathbf{A} = \begin{pmatrix} 2 & 1 \\ -3 & 0 \end{pmatrix}$ and $\mathbf{B} = \begin{pmatrix} 3 & -2 \end{pmatrix}$.

**Solution**

(a)  The matrix $\mathbf{A}$ has 2 columns and the matrix $\mathbf{B}$ has 2 rows, so the product $\mathbf{AB}$ can be formed. Since $\mathbf{A}$ has 2 rows and $\mathbf{B}$ has 3 columns, $\mathbf{AB}$ has 2 rows and 3 columns.

To find the $(1,1)$-entry of the product $\mathbf{AB}$, we take the dot product of the *first row* of $\mathbf{A}$ with the *first column* of $\mathbf{B}$:

$$(2 \times 3) + (1 \times 1) = 7.$$

Next, to find the $(2,1)$-entry of $\mathbf{AB}$, we take the dot product of the *second row* of $\mathbf{A}$ with the *first column* of $\mathbf{B}$:

$$(-3 \times 3) + (0 \times 1) = -9.$$

When evaluating a product of matrices, it is advisable to find the entries systematically, either column by column, or row by row. Here, we find the entries column by column.

Together, these give the first column of the product $\mathbf{AB}$:

$$\left( \begin{array}{ccc} 7 & * & * \\ -9 & * & * \end{array} \right).$$

To find the $(1,2)$-entry of the product $\mathbf{AB}$, we take the dot product of the *first row* of $\mathbf{A}$ with the *second column* of $\mathbf{B}$:

$$(2 \times -2) + (1 \times 1) = -3.$$

Next, to find the $(2,2)$-entry of $\mathbf{AB}$, we take the dot product of the *second row* of $\mathbf{A}$ with the *second column* of $\mathbf{B}$:

$$(-3 \times -2) + (0 \times 1) = 6.$$

We now have the second column of the product $\mathbf{AB}$:

$$\left( \begin{array}{ccc} 7 & -3 & * \\ -9 & 6 & * \end{array} \right).$$

To find the $(1,3)$-entry of the product $\mathbf{AB}$, we take the dot product of the *first row* of $\mathbf{A}$ with the *third column* of $\mathbf{B}$:

$$(2 \times 0) + (1 \times 4) = 4.$$

Next, to find the $(2,3)$-entry of $\mathbf{AB}$, we take the dot product of the *second row* of $\mathbf{A}$ with the *third column* of $\mathbf{B}$:

$$(-3 \times 0) + (0 \times 4) = 0.$$

We now have the third column of the product $\mathbf{AB}$:

$$\left( \begin{array}{ccc} 7 & -3 & 4 \\ -9 & 6 & 0 \end{array} \right).$$

Thus

$$\left( \begin{array}{cc} 2 & 1 \\ -3 & 0 \end{array} \right) \left( \begin{array}{ccc} 3 & -2 & 0 \\ 1 & 1 & 4 \end{array} \right) = \left( \begin{array}{ccc} 7 & -3 & 4 \\ -9 & 6 & 0 \end{array} \right).$$

(b)  The matrix $\mathbf{A}$ has 2 columns and the matrix $\mathbf{B}$ has 1 row, so the product $\mathbf{AB}$ is not defined.  ■

**Exercise 3.8**  Evaluate the following matrix products, where possible.

(a) $\left( \begin{array}{cc} 2 & -1 \\ 0 & 3 \\ 1 & 2 \end{array} \right) \left( \begin{array}{c} 3 \\ 2 \end{array} \right)$      (b) $\left( \begin{array}{cc} 2 & 1 \end{array} \right) \left( \begin{array}{cc} 1 & 6 \\ 0 & 2 \end{array} \right)$

(c) $\left( \begin{array}{c} 2 \\ -4 \\ 1 \end{array} \right) \left( \begin{array}{cc} 3 & 2 \\ 4 & -1 \end{array} \right)$      (d) $\left( \begin{array}{c} 1 \\ 2 \end{array} \right) \left( \begin{array}{ccc} 3 & 0 & -4 \end{array} \right)$

(e) $\left( \begin{array}{ccc} 3 & 1 & 2 \\ 0 & 5 & 1 \end{array} \right) \left( \begin{array}{ccc} -2 & 0 & 1 \\ 1 & 3 & 0 \\ 4 & 1 & -1 \end{array} \right)$

Earlier, we showed that the operation of matrix addition is both commutative and associative.

Subsection 3.1

**Exercise 3.9**   Let

$$\mathbf{A} = \begin{pmatrix} 1 & 1 \\ 3 & 2 \end{pmatrix} \quad \text{and} \quad \mathbf{B} = \begin{pmatrix} 1 & 4 \\ 2 & 1 \end{pmatrix}.$$

Calculate the products **AB** and **BA**. Comment on your findings.

You should have obtained different answers for **AB** and **BA** in Exercise 3.9; thus matrix multiplication is not commutative. This means that it is important to describe the matrix product carefully. We say that **AB** is the matrix **A** *multiplied on the right* by the matrix **B**, or the matrix **B** *multiplied on the left* by the matrix **A**.

Matrix multiplication is associative; that is, the products $(\mathbf{AB})\mathbf{C}$ and $\mathbf{A}(\mathbf{BC})$ are equal (when they can be formed).

*The associativity of matrix multiplication is proved in general in Unit LA4.*

You have seen that the distributive law holds for multiplication of a matrix by a scalar. This law also holds for multiplication of a matrix by a matrix; that is, $\mathbf{A}(\mathbf{B} + \mathbf{C}) = \mathbf{AB} + \mathbf{AC}$, whenever these products can be formed.

## Diagonal and triangular matrices

The entries of a square matrix from the top left-hand corner to the bottom right-hand corner are the *diagonal* entries; the diagonal entries form the *main diagonal* of the matrix. For a square matrix $\mathbf{A} = (a_{ij})$ of size $n \times n$, the diagonal entries are

*The main diagonal is sometimes called the leading or principal diagonal.*

$$a_{11}, \ a_{22}, \ \ldots, \ a_{nn}.$$

---

**Definition**   A **diagonal matrix** is a square matrix each of whose non-diagonal entries is zero.

---

For example, the following are diagonal matrices:

$$\begin{pmatrix} 1 & 0 \\ 0 & -2 \end{pmatrix} \quad \text{and} \quad \begin{pmatrix} 3 & 0 & 0 \\ 0 & -7 & 0 \\ 0 & 0 & 0 \end{pmatrix}.$$

To see how diagonal matrices multiply, try the following exercise.

**Exercise 3.10**   Let

$$\mathbf{A} = \begin{pmatrix} 1 & 0 \\ 0 & 7 \end{pmatrix}, \quad \mathbf{B} = \begin{pmatrix} -3 & 0 \\ 0 & 4 \end{pmatrix} \quad \text{and} \quad \mathbf{C} = \begin{pmatrix} 2 & 0 \\ 0 & 12 \end{pmatrix}.$$

Evaluate the following products.
(a) **AB**    (b) **BA**    (c) **ABC**

Notice that the product of two diagonal matrices is another diagonal matrix. Multiplying diagonal matrices is straightforward—the $i$th diagonal entry of the product is the product of the $i$th diagonal entries of the matrices being multiplied. Multiplication of *diagonal matrices* is therefore commutative.

A square matrix with each entry *below* the main diagonal equal to zero is called an *upper-triangular matrix*. Similarly, a matrix with each entry *above* the main diagonal equal to zero is called a *lower-triangular matrix*. A square row-reduced matrix is an upper-triangular matrix. A square matrix that is both upper-triangular and lower-triangular is necessarily a diagonal matrix.

**Exercise 3.11** State which of the following matrices are diagonal, upper-triangular or lower-triangular.

(a) $\begin{pmatrix} 1 & 1 & 1 \\ 0 & 2 & 2 \\ 0 & 0 & 3 \end{pmatrix}$   (b) $\begin{pmatrix} 9 & 0 \\ 0 & 0 \end{pmatrix}$

(c) $\begin{pmatrix} 0 & 0 & 1 \\ 0 & 1 & 2 \\ 1 & 2 & 3 \end{pmatrix}$   (d) $\begin{pmatrix} 1 & 0 \\ 1 & 0 \end{pmatrix}$

## Identity matrix

We have found that there are matrices corresponding to the number 0, the zero matrices $\mathbf{0}_{m,n}$. There is also a matrix corresponding to the number 1, namely, the *identity matrix*, denoted by $\mathbf{I}_n$. The subscript $n$ indicates that the matrix is an $n \times n$ matrix.

The identity matrix is written simply as $\mathbf{I}$ when the size is clear from the context.

---

**Definition** The **identity matrix** $\mathbf{I}_n$ is the $n \times n$ matrix

$$\begin{pmatrix} 1 & 0 & \cdots & 0 & 0 \\ 0 & 1 & \cdots & 0 & 0 \\ \vdots & \vdots & \ddots & \vdots & \vdots \\ 0 & 0 & \cdots & 1 & 0 \\ 0 & 0 & \cdots & 0 & 1 \end{pmatrix}.$$

Each of the entries is 0 except those on the main diagonal, which are all 1.

---

For example, the identity matrices $\mathbf{I}_2$, $\mathbf{I}_3$ and $\mathbf{I}_4$ are

$$\begin{pmatrix} 1 & 0 \\ 0 & 1 \end{pmatrix}, \quad \begin{pmatrix} 1 & 0 & 0 \\ 0 & 1 & 0 \\ 0 & 0 & 1 \end{pmatrix}, \quad \begin{pmatrix} 1 & 0 & 0 & 0 \\ 0 & 1 & 0 & 0 \\ 0 & 0 & 1 & 0 \\ 0 & 0 & 0 & 1 \end{pmatrix}.$$

If we multiply a $3 \times 2$ matrix on the left by $\mathbf{I}_3$ and then on the right by $\mathbf{I}_2$, we obtain

$$\begin{pmatrix} 1 & 0 & 0 \\ 0 & 1 & 0 \\ 0 & 0 & 1 \end{pmatrix} \begin{pmatrix} a & b \\ c & d \\ e & f \end{pmatrix} = \begin{pmatrix} a & b \\ c & d \\ e & f \end{pmatrix}$$

Here, $a$, $b$, $c$, $d$, $e$ and $f$ are any real numbers.

and

$$\begin{pmatrix} a & b \\ c & d \\ e & f \end{pmatrix} \begin{pmatrix} 1 & 0 \\ 0 & 1 \end{pmatrix} = \begin{pmatrix} a & b \\ c & d \\ e & f \end{pmatrix}.$$

In both cases, the matrix is unchanged.

---

**Theorem 3.4** Let $\mathbf{A}$ be an $m \times n$ matrix. Then

$$\mathbf{I}_m \mathbf{A} = \mathbf{A} \mathbf{I}_n = \mathbf{A}.$$

You are asked to prove Theorem 3.4 in Exercise 3.17.

---

# 3.4  Transposition of matrices

There is a simple operation that we can perform on matrices. This operation, called *transposition* or *taking the transpose*, entails interchanging the rows with the columns of the matrix. Thus the transpose of the matrix $\mathbf{A}$, denoted by $\mathbf{A}^T$, has the rows of $\mathbf{A}$ as its columns, taken in the same order. For example,

Transposition of a *square* matrix can be thought of as reflecting the matrix in the main diagonal.

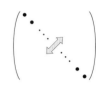

$$\begin{pmatrix} 1 & 2 & 3 \\ 4 & 5 & 6 \\ 7 & 8 & 9 \end{pmatrix}^T = \begin{pmatrix} 1 & 4 & 7 \\ 2 & 5 & 8 \\ 3 & 6 & 9 \end{pmatrix} \quad \text{and} \quad \begin{pmatrix} 2 & 7 \\ -6 & 1 \\ 0 & 4 \end{pmatrix}^T = \begin{pmatrix} 2 & -6 & 0 \\ 7 & 1 & 4 \end{pmatrix}.$$

> **Definition**   The **transpose** of an $m \times n$ matrix $\mathbf{A}$ is the $n \times m$ matrix $\mathbf{A}^T$ whose $(i, j)$-entry is the $(j, i)$-entry of $\mathbf{A}$.

**Exercise 3.12**   Write down the transpose of each of the following matrices.

(a) $\begin{pmatrix} 1 & 4 \\ 0 & 2 \\ -6 & 10 \end{pmatrix}$     (b) $\begin{pmatrix} 2 & 1 & 2 \\ 0 & 3 & -5 \\ 4 & 7 & 0 \end{pmatrix}$

(c) $\begin{pmatrix} 10 & 4 & 6 \end{pmatrix}$     (d) $\begin{pmatrix} 1 & 0 \\ 0 & 2 \end{pmatrix}$

The identity matrix $\mathbf{I}$ is not changed by taking the transpose; that is, $\mathbf{I}^T = \mathbf{I}$.

The rows of the matrix $\mathbf{A}$ form the columns of the matrix $\mathbf{A}^T$, and the columns of $\mathbf{A}^T$ form the rows of $(\mathbf{A}^T)^T$. Therefore the rows of $\mathbf{A}$ form the rows of $(\mathbf{A}^T)^T$; that is, these two matrices are equal:

$$(\mathbf{A}^T)^T = \mathbf{A}.$$

**Exercise 3.13**   Let

$$\mathbf{A} = \begin{pmatrix} 1 & 2 \\ 3 & 4 \\ 5 & 6 \end{pmatrix}, \quad \mathbf{B} = \begin{pmatrix} 7 & 8 \\ 9 & 10 \\ 11 & 12 \end{pmatrix} \quad \text{and} \quad \mathbf{C} = \begin{pmatrix} 1 & 0 \\ 1 & 1 \end{pmatrix}.$$

(a) Find $\mathbf{A}^T$, $\mathbf{B}^T$ and $(\mathbf{A} + \mathbf{B})^T$, and verify that $(\mathbf{A} + \mathbf{B})^T = \mathbf{A}^T + \mathbf{B}^T$.

(b) Find $\mathbf{C}^T$ and $(\mathbf{AC})^T$, and discover an equation relating $(\mathbf{AC})^T$, $\mathbf{A}^T$ and $\mathbf{C}^T$.

The relationships satisfied by the matrices in Exercise 3.13 hold in general. We collect together these results for the transposition of matrices in the following theorem.

> **Theorem 3.5**   Let $\mathbf{A}$ and $\mathbf{B}$ be $m \times n$ matrices. Then the following results hold:
>
> (a) $(\mathbf{A}^T)^T = \mathbf{A}$;
>
> (b) $(\mathbf{A} + \mathbf{B})^T = \mathbf{A}^T + \mathbf{B}^T$.
>
> Let $\mathbf{A}$ be an $m \times n$ matrix and $\mathbf{B}$ an $n \times p$ matrix. Then
>
> (c) $(\mathbf{AB})^T = \mathbf{B}^T \mathbf{A}^T$.

We omit the proofs: (a) and (b) are straightforward to prove.

## Symmetric matrices

Some square matrices remain unchanged when transposed. These matrices are called *symmetric* matrices, since they are symmetrical about the main diagonal.

---

**Definition**    A square matrix $\mathbf{A}$ is **symmetric** if

$$\mathbf{A}^T = \mathbf{A}.$$

---

The entries off the main diagonal of a diagonal matrix are all zero, so all diagonal matrices are symmetric, as are the following:

$$\begin{pmatrix} 3 & 1 & 1 \\ 1 & 3 & 1 \\ 1 & 1 & 3 \end{pmatrix}, \quad \begin{pmatrix} 1 & 1 \\ 1 & 1 \end{pmatrix}, \quad \begin{pmatrix} 1 & 2 & 3 & 4 \\ 2 & 5 & 6 & 7 \\ 3 & 6 & 8 & 9 \\ 4 & 7 & 9 & 10 \end{pmatrix}, \quad \begin{pmatrix} -5 & 2 \\ 2 & 3 \end{pmatrix}.$$

# 3.5  Matrix form of a system of linear equations

In this subsection we show how a system of linear equations can be expressed in *matrix form* as a product of matrices. This helps to explain why we multiply matrices in such an 'odd way'.

Consider the system of simultaneous linear equations

$$\begin{cases} x_1 + 2x_2 + 4x_3 = 6, \\ \quad\quad x_2 + x_3 = 1, \\ x_1 + 3x_2 + 5x_3 = 10. \end{cases}$$

We can write this system as a matrix equation:

$$\begin{pmatrix} x_1 + 2x_2 + 4x_3 \\ x_2 + x_3 \\ x_1 + 3x_2 + 5x_3 \end{pmatrix} = \begin{pmatrix} 6 \\ 1 \\ 10 \end{pmatrix}.$$

Now the $3 \times 1$ matrix on the left can be expressed as the product of two matrices, namely, the $3 \times 3$ matrix of the coefficients and the $3 \times 1$ matrix of the unknowns:

$$\begin{pmatrix} x_1 + 2x_2 + 4x_3 \\ x_2 + x_3 \\ x_1 + 3x_2 + 5x_3 \end{pmatrix} = \begin{pmatrix} 1 & 2 & 4 \\ 0 & 1 & 1 \\ 1 & 3 & 5 \end{pmatrix} \begin{pmatrix} x_1 \\ x_2 \\ x_3 \end{pmatrix}.$$

Thus we have the matrix equation

$$\begin{pmatrix} 1 & 2 & 4 \\ 0 & 1 & 1 \\ 1 & 3 & 5 \end{pmatrix} \begin{pmatrix} x_1 \\ x_2 \\ x_3 \end{pmatrix} = \begin{pmatrix} 6 \\ 1 \\ 10 \end{pmatrix}.$$

Similarly, we can express any system of simultaneous linear equations

$$\begin{cases} a_{11}x_1 + a_{12}x_2 + \cdots + a_{1n}x_n = b_1, \\ a_{21}x_1 + a_{22}x_2 + \cdots + a_{2n}x_n = b_2, \\ \quad\vdots \quad\quad\quad \vdots \quad\quad\quad \vdots \quad\quad \vdots \\ a_{m1}x_1 + a_{m2}x_2 + \cdots + a_{mn}x_n = b_m, \end{cases}$$

as a matrix product.

Let the matrix of coefficients be $\mathbf{A}$, the *coefficient matrix* of the system, that is,

$$\mathbf{A} = \begin{pmatrix} a_{11} & a_{12} & \cdots & a_{1n} \\ a_{21} & a_{22} & \cdots & a_{2n} \\ \vdots & \vdots & & \vdots \\ a_{m1} & a_{m2} & \cdots & a_{mn} \end{pmatrix}.$$

Let the matrix of unknowns be $\mathbf{x}$, and let the matrix of constant terms be $\mathbf{b}$, so

$$\mathbf{x} = \begin{pmatrix} x_1 \\ x_2 \\ \vdots \\ x_n \end{pmatrix} \quad \text{and} \quad \mathbf{b} = \begin{pmatrix} b_1 \\ b_2 \\ \vdots \\ b_m \end{pmatrix}.$$

The system can then be expressed in **matrix form** as

$$\mathbf{Ax} = \mathbf{b},$$

or in full as

$$\begin{pmatrix} a_{11} & a_{12} & \cdots & a_{1n} \\ a_{21} & a_{22} & \cdots & a_{2n} \\ \vdots & \vdots & & \vdots \\ a_{m1} & a_{m2} & \cdots & a_{mn} \end{pmatrix} \begin{pmatrix} x_1 \\ x_2 \\ \vdots \\ x_n \end{pmatrix} = \begin{pmatrix} b_1 \\ b_2 \\ \vdots \\ b_m \end{pmatrix}.$$

# Further exercises

**Exercise 3.14**   Let $\mathbf{A} = \begin{pmatrix} 1 & 6 \\ 3 & -4 \end{pmatrix}$ and $\mathbf{B} = \begin{pmatrix} 2 & -3 \\ 0 & 7 \end{pmatrix}$. Evaluate the following.

(a) $\mathbf{A} + \mathbf{B}$    (b) $\mathbf{A} - \mathbf{B}$    (c) $\mathbf{B} - \mathbf{A}$    (d) $\mathbf{AB}$    (e) $\mathbf{BA}$

(f) $\mathbf{A}^2$    (g) $\mathbf{A}^T$    (h) $\mathbf{B}^T$    (i) $\mathbf{A}^T\mathbf{B}^T$

**Exercise 3.15**   Suppose that we are given matrices of the following sizes:

$$\mathbf{A}: 2 \times 1, \quad \mathbf{B}: 4 \times 3, \quad \mathbf{C}: 3 \times 2, \quad \mathbf{D}: 1 \times 4,$$
$$\mathbf{E}: 3 \times 3, \quad \mathbf{F}: 3 \times 4, \quad \mathbf{G}: 2 \times 4.$$

Which of the following expressions are defined? Give the size of the resulting matrix for those that are defined.

(a) $\mathbf{FB} + \mathbf{E}$    (b) $\mathbf{GF}^T - \mathbf{ADB}$    (c) $\mathbf{BF} - (\mathbf{FB})^T$

(d) $\mathbf{C}(\mathbf{AD} + \mathbf{G})$    (e) $(\mathbf{CA})^T\mathbf{D}$    (f) $\mathbf{E}^T\mathbf{B}^T\mathbf{G}^T\mathbf{C}^T$

**Exercise 3.16**   Prove the distributive law, that for all matrices $\mathbf{A}$ and $\mathbf{B}$ of the same size, and all scalars $k$,    *This is Theorem 3.3.*

$$k(\mathbf{A} + \mathbf{B}) = k\mathbf{A} + k\mathbf{B}.$$

**Exercise 3.17**   Let $\mathbf{A} = (a_{ij})$ be an $m \times n$ matrix. Prove that $\mathbf{I}_m\mathbf{A} = \mathbf{A}$    *This is Theorem 3.4.*
and $\mathbf{AI}_n = \mathbf{A}$.

Hint: Notice that the entries in the $i$th row of $\mathbf{I}_m$ are all 0 except the entry in the $i$th position, which is 1.

# 4    Matrix inverses

After working through this section, you should be able to:

(a) understand what is meant by an *invertible* matrix;

(b) understand that the set of $n \times n$ invertible matrices forms a group under matrix multiplication;

(c) determine whether or not a given matrix is invertible and, if it is, find its inverse;

(d) state the relationship between the invertibility of a square matrix and the number of solutions of a system of linear equations with that square matrix as its coefficient matrix;

(e) understand the connections between elementary row operations and elementary matrices.

## 4.1  Matrix inverses

In Section 3 we saw that many of the properties of ordinary arithmetic have analogues in matrix algebra. We now consider the extent to which a further important property of ordinary arithmetic is mirrored in matrix algebra. You are familiar with the fact that, for each non-zero real number $a$, there exists a number $b$, called the *reciprocal* or *multiplicative inverse* of $a$, such that

For example, the reciprocal of 4 is $\frac{1}{4}$.

$$ab = 1 \quad \text{and} \quad ba = 1.$$

Each non-zero real number $a$ has exactly one reciprocal, and we denote it by $a^{-1}$ or $1/a$.

The role played by the number 1 in ordinary arithmetic is played in matrix algebra by the identity matrix $\mathbf{I}$; therefore we make the following definition.

---

**Definition**    Let $\mathbf{A}$ be a square matrix, and suppose that there exists a matrix $\mathbf{B}$ of the same size such that

$$\mathbf{AB} = \mathbf{I} \quad \text{and} \quad \mathbf{BA} = \mathbf{I}.$$

Then $\mathbf{B}$ is an **inverse** of $\mathbf{A}$.

---

You need both these equations for $\mathbf{B}$ to be the inverse of $\mathbf{A}$. One alone is not enough.

Notice that we restrict the definition to *square* matrices. It can be proved that if $\mathbf{A}$ is not a square matrix, then $\mathbf{AB}$ and $\mathbf{BA}$ cannot *both* be identity matrices—so the definition cannot be extended to non-square matrices.

For example,

$$\begin{pmatrix} 3 & -1 \\ -5 & 2 \end{pmatrix} \text{ is an inverse of } \begin{pmatrix} 2 & 1 \\ 5 & 3 \end{pmatrix}$$

since

$$\begin{pmatrix} 2 & 1 \\ 5 & 3 \end{pmatrix} \begin{pmatrix} 3 & -1 \\ -5 & 2 \end{pmatrix} = \begin{pmatrix} 1 & 0 \\ 0 & 1 \end{pmatrix}$$

and

$$\begin{pmatrix} 3 & -1 \\ -5 & 2 \end{pmatrix} \begin{pmatrix} 2 & 1 \\ 5 & 3 \end{pmatrix} = \begin{pmatrix} 1 & 0 \\ 0 & 1 \end{pmatrix}.$$

Similarly,

$$\begin{pmatrix} -1 & -5 & -2 \\ 0 & 2 & 1 \\ -2 & 1 & 1 \end{pmatrix} \text{ is an inverse of } \begin{pmatrix} 1 & 3 & -1 \\ -2 & -5 & 1 \\ 4 & 11 & -2 \end{pmatrix}$$

since

$$\begin{pmatrix} 1 & 3 & -1 \\ -2 & -5 & 1 \\ 4 & 11 & -2 \end{pmatrix} \begin{pmatrix} -1 & -5 & -2 \\ 0 & 2 & 1 \\ -2 & 1 & 1 \end{pmatrix} = \begin{pmatrix} 1 & 0 & 0 \\ 0 & 1 & 0 \\ 0 & 0 & 1 \end{pmatrix}$$

and

$$\begin{pmatrix} -1 & -5 & -2 \\ 0 & 2 & 1 \\ -2 & 1 & 1 \end{pmatrix} \begin{pmatrix} 1 & 3 & -1 \\ -2 & -5 & 1 \\ 4 & 11 & -2 \end{pmatrix} = \begin{pmatrix} 1 & 0 & 0 \\ 0 & 1 & 0 \\ 0 & 0 & 1 \end{pmatrix}.$$

Just as a real number has at most one reciprocal, a square matrix has at most one inverse, as we now prove.

---

**Theorem 4.1**    A square matrix has at most one inverse.

---

**Proof**    Let $\mathbf{A}$ be a square matrix, and suppose that $\mathbf{B}$ and $\mathbf{C}$ are both inverses of $\mathbf{A}$. Then $\mathbf{AB} = \mathbf{I}$ and $\mathbf{CA} = \mathbf{I}$.

Multiplying the equation $\mathbf{AB} = \mathbf{I}$ on the left by $\mathbf{C}$, we have

$$\mathbf{C}(\mathbf{AB}) = \mathbf{CI} = \mathbf{C},$$

while multiplying the equation $\mathbf{CA} = \mathbf{I}$ on the right by $\mathbf{B}$ gives

$$(\mathbf{CA})\mathbf{B} = \mathbf{IB} = \mathbf{B}.$$

This shows us why we need both $\mathbf{AB} = \mathbf{I}$ and $\mathbf{BA} = \mathbf{I}$ in the definition on page 41.

Since matrix multiplication is associative, it follows that $\mathbf{B} = \mathbf{C}$. ∎

Now, every non-zero real number has a reciprocal, so it is natural to ask whether or not every non-zero square matrix has an inverse. The next exercise demonstrates that the answer to this question is *no*—it gives an example of a non-zero square matrix with no inverse.

Certainly a square zero matrix has no inverse (just as the real number 0 has no reciprocal). This is easy to see: if $\mathbf{0}$ is a square zero matrix, then any product of $\mathbf{0}$ and another matrix is a zero matrix, so there is no matrix $\mathbf{B}$ such that $\mathbf{0B} = \mathbf{I}$.

**Exercise 4.1**    Let $\mathbf{A} = \begin{pmatrix} 1 & -1 \\ -1 & 1 \end{pmatrix}$.

Prove that there is no matrix $\mathbf{B} = \begin{pmatrix} a & b \\ c & d \end{pmatrix}$ such that $\mathbf{AB} = \mathbf{I}$.

In fact, there are many non-zero square matrices with no inverse. The next theorem gives an infinite class of such matrices.

---

**Theorem 4.2**    A square matrix with a zero row has no inverse.

---

**Proof**    Let $\mathbf{A}$ be a square matrix one of whose rows, say row $i$, is a zero row. Then if $\mathbf{B}$ is any matrix of the same size as $\mathbf{A}$, the $(i, i)$-entry of $\mathbf{AB}$ is 0, since it is equal to the dot product of row $i$ of $\mathbf{A}$ (a zero row) with column $i$ of $\mathbf{B}$. But the $(i, i)$-entry of $\mathbf{I}$ is 1, which shows that there is no matrix $\mathbf{B}$ such that $\mathbf{AB} = \mathbf{I}$. Hence $\mathbf{A}$ has no inverse. ∎

**Definition**    A square matrix that has an inverse is **invertible**.

We denote the unique inverse of an invertible matrix $\mathbf{A}$ by $\mathbf{A}^{-1}$. Thus, for any invertible matrix $\mathbf{A}$,

$$\mathbf{A}\mathbf{A}^{-1} = \mathbf{I} \quad \text{and} \quad \mathbf{A}^{-1}\mathbf{A} = \mathbf{I}.$$

Notice from these equations that if $\mathbf{A}$ is an invertible matrix, then $\mathbf{A}^{-1}$ is also invertible, with inverse $\mathbf{A}$; that is,

$$(\mathbf{A}^{-1})^{-1} = \mathbf{A}.$$

In other words, $\mathbf{A}$ and $\mathbf{A}^{-1}$ are *inverses of each other*.

This is similar to inverses in $\mathbb{R}$, where $(a^{-1})^{-1} = a$.

The next example and the following exercises give some other useful facts about matrix inverses.

**Example 4.1**    Let $\mathbf{A}$ be an invertible matrix. Prove that $\mathbf{A}^T$ is invertible, and that $(\mathbf{A}^T)^{-1} = (\mathbf{A}^{-1})^T$.

We introduced $\mathbf{A}^T$, the *transpose* of $\mathbf{A}$, in Subsection 3.4.

**Solution**    To prove that $\mathbf{A}^T$ is invertible, with inverse $(\mathbf{A}^{-1})^T$, we have to show that

$$\mathbf{A}^T(\mathbf{A}^{-1})^T = \mathbf{I} \quad \text{and} \quad (\mathbf{A}^{-1})^T\mathbf{A}^T = \mathbf{I}.$$

But

$$\mathbf{A}^T(\mathbf{A}^{-1})^T = (\mathbf{A}^{-1}\mathbf{A})^T = \mathbf{I}^T = \mathbf{I},$$

Recall from Subsection 3.4 that $(\mathbf{A}\mathbf{B})^T = \mathbf{B}^T\mathbf{A}^T$.

and, similarly,

$$(\mathbf{A}^{-1})^T\mathbf{A}^T = (\mathbf{A}\mathbf{A}^{-1})^T = \mathbf{I}^T = \mathbf{I}.$$

The required result follows.    ■

**Exercise 4.2**    Prove that $\mathbf{I}$ is invertible, and that $\mathbf{I}^{-1} = \mathbf{I}$.

**Exercise 4.3**    Let $\mathbf{A}$ and $\mathbf{B}$ be invertible matrices of the same size. Prove that $\mathbf{A}\mathbf{B}$ is invertible, and that $(\mathbf{A}\mathbf{B})^{-1} = \mathbf{B}^{-1}\mathbf{A}^{-1}$.

Notice the reversal of the order of the matrices in the identity

$$(\mathbf{A}\mathbf{B})^{-1} = \mathbf{B}^{-1}\mathbf{A}^{-1}.$$

The result of Exercise 4.3 extends to products of any number of matrices.

**Theorem 4.3**    Let $\mathbf{A}_1, \mathbf{A}_2, \ldots, \mathbf{A}_k$ be invertible matrices of the same size. Then the product $\mathbf{A}_1\mathbf{A}_2 \cdots \mathbf{A}_k$ is invertible, with

$$(\mathbf{A}_1\mathbf{A}_2 \cdots \mathbf{A}_k)^{-1} = \mathbf{A}_k^{-1}\mathbf{A}_{k-1}^{-1} \cdots \mathbf{A}_1^{-1}.$$

This can be proved using the result of Exercise 4.3 and mathematical induction.

Using the results of the above exercises, we can show that the set of all invertible matrices of a particular size forms a group under matrix multiplication.

The group axioms were defined in Unit GTA1.

**Theorem 4.4**    The set of all invertible $n \times n$ matrices forms a group under matrix multiplication.

The set of *all* $n \times n$ matrices *does not* form a group under matrix multiplication: it fails to satisfy the axiom G3 INVERSES, since, for example, the $n \times n$ zero matrix has no inverse.

**Proof**　We must check that the four group axioms hold.

Exercise 4.3 tells us that the group axiom G1 CLOSURE holds for this set.

Exercise 4.2 shows that $\mathbf{I}$ is a member of the set, so the set contains an identity element. In other words, the axiom G2 IDENTITY holds.

Each matrix in the set has an inverse, and this inverse is itself invertible and therefore also in the set; so the axiom G3 INVERSES holds.

Remember, $(\mathbf{A}^{-1})^{-1} = \mathbf{A}$.

Finally, we know from Section 3 that matrix multiplication is associative, so the axiom G4 ASSOCIATIVITY holds.　■

## 4.2 Invertibility Theorem

The following two questions may already have occurred to you as you worked through the previous subsection. First, how can we determine whether or not a given square matrix is invertible? Second, if we know that a matrix is invertible, how can we find its inverse? The next theorem answers both questions.

> **Theorem 4.5　Invertibility Theorem**
>
> (a) A square matrix is invertible if and only if its row-reduced form is $\mathbf{I}$.
>
> (b) Any sequence of elementary row operations that transforms a matrix $\mathbf{A}$ to $\mathbf{I}$ also transforms $\mathbf{I}$ to $\mathbf{A}^{-1}$.

We prove the Invertibility Theorem in Subsection 4.5.

To illustrate this theorem, consider the matrix $\mathbf{A} = \begin{pmatrix} 1 & 3 \\ 2 & 9 \end{pmatrix}$. Suppose that we wish to determine whether or not $\mathbf{A}$ is invertible and, if it is, to find $\mathbf{A}^{-1}$.

Below, on the left, we row-reduce $\mathbf{A}$ in the usual way. On the right, we perform the same sequence of elementary row operations on the $2 \times 2$ identity matrix.

$$
\begin{array}{ll}
\mathbf{r}_1 \\
\mathbf{r}_2
\end{array}
\begin{pmatrix} 1 & 3 \\ 2 & 9 \end{pmatrix}
\qquad
\begin{array}{ll}
\mathbf{r}_1 \\
\mathbf{r}_2
\end{array}
\begin{pmatrix} 1 & 0 \\ 0 & 1 \end{pmatrix}
$$

$$
\mathbf{r}_2 \to \mathbf{r}_2 - 2\mathbf{r}_1 \begin{pmatrix} 1 & 3 \\ 0 & 3 \end{pmatrix}
\qquad
\mathbf{r}_2 \to \mathbf{r}_2 - 2\mathbf{r}_1 \begin{pmatrix} 1 & 0 \\ -2 & 1 \end{pmatrix}
$$

$$
\mathbf{r}_2 \to \tfrac{1}{3}\mathbf{r}_2 \begin{pmatrix} 1 & 3 \\ 0 & 1 \end{pmatrix}
\qquad
\mathbf{r}_2 \to \tfrac{1}{3}\mathbf{r}_2 \begin{pmatrix} 1 & 0 \\ -\tfrac{2}{3} & \tfrac{1}{3} \end{pmatrix}
$$

$$
\mathbf{r}_1 \to \mathbf{r}_1 - 3\mathbf{r}_2 \begin{pmatrix} 1 & 0 \\ 0 & 1 \end{pmatrix}
\qquad
\mathbf{r}_1 \to \mathbf{r}_1 - 3\mathbf{r}_2 \begin{pmatrix} 3 & -1 \\ -\tfrac{2}{3} & \tfrac{1}{3} \end{pmatrix}
$$

The row-reduced form of $\mathbf{A}$ is $\mathbf{I}$, so we conclude from the first part of the Invertibility Theorem that $\mathbf{A}$ is an invertible matrix.

By the second part of the Invertibility Theorem, the final matrix on the right above must be $\mathbf{A}^{-1}$; that is,

$$
\mathbf{A}^{-1} = \begin{pmatrix} 3 & -1 \\ -\tfrac{2}{3} & \tfrac{1}{3} \end{pmatrix}.
$$

You should check that this matrix is indeed the inverse of $\mathbf{A}$.

When we apply the Invertibility Theorem to find the inverse of a matrix $\mathbf{A}$, we have to perform the same sequence of elementary row operations on both $\mathbf{A}$ and $\mathbf{I}$. We can do this conveniently in the following way. We begin by writing $\mathbf{A}$ and $\mathbf{I}$ alongside each other, separated by a vertical line, giving a larger matrix which we may denote by $(\mathbf{A} \mid \mathbf{I})$. We then row-reduce $(\mathbf{A} \mid \mathbf{I})$ in the usual way. When we do this, the above calculation looks like this:

$$
\begin{matrix}
\mathbf{r}_1 \\
\mathbf{r}_2
\end{matrix}
\qquad
\left( \begin{array}{cc|cc}
1 & 3 & 1 & 0 \\
2 & 9 & 0 & 1
\end{array} \right)
$$

$$
\mathbf{r}_2 \to \mathbf{r}_2 - 2\mathbf{r}_1
\qquad
\left( \begin{array}{cc|cc}
1 & 3 & 1 & 0 \\
0 & 3 & -2 & 1
\end{array} \right)
$$

$$
\mathbf{r}_2 \to \tfrac{1}{3}\mathbf{r}_2
\qquad
\left( \begin{array}{cc|cc}
1 & 3 & 1 & 0 \\
0 & 1 & -\tfrac{2}{3} & \tfrac{1}{3}
\end{array} \right)
$$

$$
\mathbf{r}_1 \to \mathbf{r}_1 - 3\mathbf{r}_2
\qquad
\left( \begin{array}{cc|cc}
1 & 0 & 3 & -1 \\
0 & 1 & -\tfrac{2}{3} & \tfrac{1}{3}
\end{array} \right).
$$

Thus the Invertibility Theorem gives us the following strategy.

---

**Strategy 4.1**   To determine whether or not a given square matrix $\mathbf{A}$ is invertible, and find its inverse if it is.

Write down $(\mathbf{A} \mid \mathbf{I})$, and row-reduce it until the left half is in row-reduced form.

- If the left half is the identity matrix, then the right half is $\mathbf{A}^{-1}$.
- Otherwise, $\mathbf{A}$ is not invertible.

---

You may find it helpful to remember the following scheme:

$$(\mathbf{A} \mid \mathbf{I})$$
$$\downarrow$$
$$(\mathbf{I} \mid \mathbf{A}^{-1}).$$

*Remark*   Strategy 4.1 is most useful for matrices of size $3 \times 3$ and larger. In Section 5 we give a quick method for determining whether or not a $2 \times 2$ matrix is invertible, and for writing down its inverse if it is.

**Example 4.2**   Determine whether or not each of the following matrices is invertible, and find the inverse if it exists.

(a) $\begin{pmatrix} 1 & 1 & 2 \\ -1 & 0 & -4 \\ 3 & 2 & 10 \end{pmatrix}$
(b) $\begin{pmatrix} 1 & 3 & 5 \\ 3 & 1 & 7 \\ 2 & 4 & 8 \end{pmatrix}$

**Solution**   We use Strategy 4.1.

(a) We form the matrix $(\mathbf{A} \mid \mathbf{I})$, and row-reduce it in the usual way.

$$
\begin{matrix}
\mathbf{r}_1 \\
\mathbf{r}_2 \\
\mathbf{r}_3
\end{matrix}
\qquad
\left( \begin{array}{ccc|ccc}
1 & 1 & 2 & 1 & 0 & 0 \\
-1 & 0 & -4 & 0 & 1 & 0 \\
3 & 2 & 10 & 0 & 0 & 1
\end{array} \right)
$$

$$
\begin{matrix}
\mathbf{r}_2 \to \mathbf{r}_2 + \mathbf{r}_1 \\
\mathbf{r}_3 \to \mathbf{r}_3 - 3\mathbf{r}_1
\end{matrix}
\qquad
\left( \begin{array}{ccc|ccc}
1 & 1 & 2 & 1 & 0 & 0 \\
0 & 1 & -2 & 1 & 1 & 0 \\
0 & -1 & 4 & -3 & 0 & 1
\end{array} \right)
$$

$$
\begin{matrix}
\mathbf{r}_1 \to \mathbf{r}_1 - \mathbf{r}_2 \\
\\
\mathbf{r}_3 \to \mathbf{r}_3 + \mathbf{r}_2
\end{matrix}
\qquad
\left( \begin{array}{ccc|ccc}
1 & 0 & 4 & 0 & -1 & 0 \\
0 & 1 & -2 & 1 & 1 & 0 \\
0 & 0 & 2 & -2 & 1 & 1
\end{array} \right)
$$

$$
\mathbf{r}_3 \to \tfrac{1}{2}\mathbf{r}_3
\qquad
\left( \begin{array}{ccc|ccc}
1 & 0 & 4 & 0 & -1 & 0 \\
0 & 1 & -2 & 1 & 1 & 0 \\
0 & 0 & 1 & -1 & \tfrac{1}{2} & \tfrac{1}{2}
\end{array} \right)
$$

$$
\begin{matrix}
\mathbf{r}_1 \to \mathbf{r}_1 - 4\mathbf{r}_3 \\
\mathbf{r}_2 \to \mathbf{r}_2 + 2\mathbf{r}_3
\end{matrix}
\qquad
\left( \begin{array}{ccc|ccc}
1 & 0 & 0 & 4 & -3 & -2 \\
0 & 1 & 0 & -1 & 2 & 1 \\
0 & 0 & 1 & -1 & \tfrac{1}{2} & \tfrac{1}{2}
\end{array} \right)
$$

The left half has been reduced to $\mathbf{I}$, so the given matrix is invertible; its inverse is given by the right half, that is,

$$\begin{pmatrix} 4 & -3 & -2 \\ -1 & 2 & 1 \\ -1 & \frac{1}{2} & \frac{1}{2} \end{pmatrix}.$$

(b)　We row-reduce $(\mathbf{A} \mid \mathbf{I})$.

$$\begin{array}{l} \mathbf{r}_1 \\ \mathbf{r}_2 \\ \mathbf{r}_3 \end{array} \qquad \left(\begin{array}{ccc|ccc} 1 & 3 & 5 & 1 & 0 & 0 \\ 3 & 1 & 7 & 0 & 1 & 0 \\ 2 & 4 & 8 & 0 & 0 & 1 \end{array}\right)$$

$$\begin{array}{l} \mathbf{r}_2 \to \mathbf{r}_2 - 3\mathbf{r}_1 \\ \mathbf{r}_3 \to \mathbf{r}_3 - 2\mathbf{r}_1 \end{array} \qquad \left(\begin{array}{ccc|ccc} 1 & 3 & 5 & 1 & 0 & 0 \\ 0 & -8 & -8 & -3 & 1 & 0 \\ 0 & -2 & -2 & -2 & 0 & 1 \end{array}\right)$$

$$\mathbf{r}_2 \to -\tfrac{1}{8}\mathbf{r}_2 \qquad \left(\begin{array}{ccc|ccc} 1 & 3 & 5 & 1 & 0 & 0 \\ 0 & 1 & 1 & \frac{3}{8} & -\frac{1}{8} & 0 \\ 0 & -2 & -2 & -2 & 0 & 1 \end{array}\right)$$

$$\begin{array}{l} \mathbf{r}_1 \to \mathbf{r}_1 - 3\mathbf{r}_2 \\ \\ \mathbf{r}_3 \to \mathbf{r}_3 + 2\mathbf{r}_2 \end{array} \qquad \left(\begin{array}{ccc|ccc} 1 & 0 & 2 & -\frac{1}{8} & \frac{3}{8} & 0 \\ 0 & 1 & 1 & \frac{3}{8} & -\frac{1}{8} & 0 \\ 0 & 0 & 0 & -\frac{5}{4} & -\frac{1}{4} & 1 \end{array}\right)$$

The left half is now in row-reduced form, but is not the identity matrix. Therefore the given matrix is not invertible.　∎

*Remark*　If it becomes clear while you are row-reducing $(\mathbf{A} \mid \mathbf{I})$ that the left half will not reduce to the identity matrix (for example, if a zero row appears in the left half), then you can stop the row-reduction immediately, and conclude that $\mathbf{A}$ is not invertible. There is no point in continuing until the left half is in row-reduced form.

**Exercise 4.4**　Use Strategy 4.1 to determine whether or not each of the following matrices is invertible, and find the inverse if it exists.

(a) $\begin{pmatrix} 2 & 4 \\ 4 & 1 \end{pmatrix}$　(b) $\begin{pmatrix} 1 & 1 & -4 \\ 2 & 1 & -6 \\ -3 & -1 & 9 \end{pmatrix}$　(c) $\begin{pmatrix} 2 & 4 & 6 \\ 1 & 2 & 4 \\ 5 & 10 & 5 \end{pmatrix}$

# 4.3　Invertibility and systems of linear equations

We can use matrix inverses to give us another method for solving certain systems of linear equations.

Consider the system

$$\begin{cases} 2x + 4y = 10, \\ 4x + y = 6. \end{cases}$$

We solved this system by Gauss–Jordan elimination in Example 1.1.

This system may be expressed in matrix form as

$$\begin{pmatrix} 2 & 4 \\ 4 & 1 \end{pmatrix} \begin{pmatrix} x \\ y \end{pmatrix} = \begin{pmatrix} 10 \\ 6 \end{pmatrix}.$$

The coefficient matrix $\begin{pmatrix} 2 & 4 \\ 4 & 1 \end{pmatrix}$ is invertible, with inverse $\begin{pmatrix} -\frac{1}{14} & \frac{2}{7} \\ \frac{2}{7} & -\frac{1}{7} \end{pmatrix}$.

See Exercise 4.4(a).

Multiplying both sides of the matrix form of the system on the left by the inverse of the coefficient matrix, we obtain

$$\begin{pmatrix} -\frac{1}{14} & \frac{2}{7} \\ \frac{2}{7} & -\frac{1}{7} \end{pmatrix} \begin{pmatrix} 2 & 4 \\ 4 & 1 \end{pmatrix} \begin{pmatrix} x \\ y \end{pmatrix} = \begin{pmatrix} -\frac{1}{14} & \frac{2}{7} \\ \frac{2}{7} & -\frac{1}{7} \end{pmatrix} \begin{pmatrix} 10 \\ 6 \end{pmatrix},$$

that is,

$$\begin{pmatrix} 1 & 0 \\ 0 & 1 \end{pmatrix} \begin{pmatrix} x \\ y \end{pmatrix} = \begin{pmatrix} 1 \\ 2 \end{pmatrix},$$

or

$$\begin{pmatrix} x \\ y \end{pmatrix} = \begin{pmatrix} 1 \\ 2 \end{pmatrix}.$$

So the system has the unique solution $\begin{pmatrix} x \\ y \end{pmatrix} = \begin{pmatrix} 1 \\ 2 \end{pmatrix}$; that is, $x = 1$, $y = 2$.

In general, suppose that $\mathbf{Ax} = \mathbf{b}$ is the matrix form of a system of linear equations, and that the coefficient matrix $\mathbf{A}$ is invertible. Then we can multiply both sides of the equation $\mathbf{Ax} = \mathbf{b}$ on the left by $\mathbf{A}^{-1}$ to yield $\mathbf{A}^{-1}\mathbf{Ax} = \mathbf{A}^{-1}\mathbf{b}$; that is, $\mathbf{x} = \mathbf{A}^{-1}\mathbf{b}$. It seems, then, that the system has the unique solution $\mathbf{x} = \mathbf{A}^{-1}\mathbf{b}$.

However, we have to be careful before making this claim. Whenever we manipulate an equation in order to solve it, we have to be sure that the manipulation yields a second equation *equivalent* to the first (otherwise the two equations might have different solution sets).

In this case, we have to be sure that

$$\mathbf{Ax} = \mathbf{b} \quad \text{if and only if} \quad \mathbf{x} = \mathbf{A}^{-1}\mathbf{b}.$$

We showed above that if $\mathbf{Ax} = \mathbf{b}$, then multiplying both sides on the left by $\mathbf{A}^{-1}$ yields $\mathbf{x} = \mathbf{A}^{-1}\mathbf{b}$; in other words, we proved that $\mathbf{Ax} = \mathbf{b}$ implies $\mathbf{x} = \mathbf{A}^{-1}\mathbf{b}$. It remains to prove that $\mathbf{x} = \mathbf{A}^{-1}\mathbf{b}$ implies $\mathbf{Ax} = \mathbf{b}$, and fortunately this is just as easy: if $\mathbf{x} = \mathbf{A}^{-1}\mathbf{b}$, then multiplying both sides of this equation on the left by $\mathbf{A}$ yields $\mathbf{Ax} = \mathbf{AA}^{-1}\mathbf{b}$; that is, $\mathbf{Ax} = \mathbf{b}$.

So multiplying both sides of $\mathbf{Ax} = \mathbf{b}$ on the left by $\mathbf{A}^{-1}$ *does* yield an equivalent equation. We have proved the following theorem.

> **Theorem 4.6**  Let $\mathbf{A}$ be an invertible matrix. Then the system of linear equations $\mathbf{Ax} = \mathbf{b}$ has the unique solution $\mathbf{x} = \mathbf{A}^{-1}\mathbf{b}$.

**Exercise 4.5**  Use Theorem 4.6 to solve the following system of linear equations:

$$\begin{cases} x + y + 2z = 1, \\ -x \quad\;\; - 4z = 2, \\ 3x + 2y + 10z = -1. \end{cases}$$

Hint: The inverse of the matrix $\begin{pmatrix} 1 & 1 & 2 \\ -1 & 0 & -4 \\ 3 & 2 & 10 \end{pmatrix}$ is $\begin{pmatrix} 4 & -3 & -2 \\ -1 & 2 & 1 \\ -1 & \frac{1}{2} & \frac{1}{2} \end{pmatrix}$.  We calculated this inverse in Example 4.2(a).

*Remark*   In general, it is worth using the method of Theorem 4.6 only if we have already calculated the inverse of the coefficient matrix. If we do not know the inverse of the coefficient matrix, then the Gauss–Jordan elimination method of Section 2 is usually quicker.

Theorem 4.6 shows, in particular, that if the coefficient matrix $\mathbf{A}$ of a system of linear equations $\mathbf{Ax} = \mathbf{b}$ is invertible, then the system has a *unique* solution. The converse of this result is also true—we prove this in the next theorem.

This theorem gives some important relationships between the invertibility of a matrix and the number of solutions of systems of linear equations with that matrix as coefficient matrix. The theorem states that the three conditions are *equivalent*: any one of the conditions implies any other one.

To use the method of Theorem 4.6 to solve $\mathbf{Ax} = \mathbf{b}$, where $\mathbf{A}$ is an $n \times n$ invertible matrix, we first invert $\mathbf{A}$. This involves row-reducing the matrix $(\mathbf{A} \mid \mathbf{I})$. We then calculate the matrix product $\mathbf{A}^{-1}\mathbf{b}$. The method of Section 2 involves only row-reducing the matrix $(\mathbf{A} \mid \mathbf{b})$.

---

**Theorem 4.7**   Let $\mathbf{A}$ be an $n \times n$ matrix. Then the following statements are equivalent.

(a)  $\mathbf{A}$ is invertible.

(b)  The system $\mathbf{Ax} = \mathbf{b}$ has a unique solution for each $n \times 1$ matrix $\mathbf{b}$.

(c)  The system $\mathbf{Ax} = \mathbf{0}$ has only the trivial solution.

---

**Proof**   We show that $(a) \Rightarrow (b)$, $(b) \Rightarrow (c)$ and $(c) \Rightarrow (a)$, which shows that the conditions are equivalent.

$(a) \Rightarrow (b)$
Suppose that $\mathbf{A}$ is an invertible $n \times n$ matrix. Then, by Theorem 4.6, for any $n \times 1$ matrix $\mathbf{b}$, the system $\mathbf{Ax} = \mathbf{b}$ has the unique solution $\mathbf{x} = \mathbf{A}^{-1}\mathbf{b}$.

$(b) \Rightarrow (c)$
Suppose that the system $\mathbf{Ax} = \mathbf{b}$ has a unique solution for each $n \times 1$ matrix $\mathbf{b}$. Then, in particular, the homogeneous system $\mathbf{Ax} = \mathbf{0}$ has a unique solution. But every homogeneous system has the trivial solution; thus this unique solution must be the trivial one.

$(c) \Rightarrow (a)$
Suppose that the system $\mathbf{Ax} = \mathbf{0}$ has only the trivial solution. Then row-reducing the augmented matrix

$$\left(\begin{array}{cccc|c} a_{11} & a_{12} & \cdots & a_{1n} & 0 \\ a_{21} & a_{22} & \cdots & a_{2n} & 0 \\ \vdots & \vdots & & \vdots & \vdots \\ a_{m1} & a_{m2} & \cdots & a_{mn} & 0 \end{array}\right)$$

of the system must yield

$$\left(\begin{array}{cccc|c} 1 & 0 & \cdots & 0 & 0 \\ 0 & 1 & \cdots & 0 & 0 \\ \vdots & \vdots & \ddots & \vdots & \vdots \\ 0 & 0 & \cdots & 1 & 0 \end{array}\right),$$

since this is the row-reduced matrix that corresponds to each unknown being 0. If we now ignore the last column of each of the matrices appearing in this row-reduction, we are left with a reduction of $\mathbf{A}$ to $\mathbf{I}$. Hence, by the Invertibility Theorem, $\mathbf{A}$ is invertible.   ∎

# 4.4 Elementary matrices

In this subsection we introduce and study a class of square matrices associated with elementary row operations.

We shall use these matrices and their properties in Subsection 4.5, to help us prove the Invertibility Theorem. We shall also find them useful later.

Consider the following matrices:

$$\begin{pmatrix} 0 & 1 & 0 \\ 1 & 0 & 0 \\ 0 & 0 & 1 \end{pmatrix}, \quad \begin{pmatrix} 1 & 0 & 0 \\ 0 & 5 & 0 \\ 0 & 0 & 1 \end{pmatrix}, \quad \begin{pmatrix} 1 & 0 & 0 \\ 0 & 1 & 0 \\ 0 & 2 & 1 \end{pmatrix}.$$

They are obtained by performing, on the $3 \times 3$ identity matrix, the elementary row operations $\mathbf{r}_1 \leftrightarrow \mathbf{r}_2$, $\mathbf{r}_2 \to 5\mathbf{r}_2$ and $\mathbf{r}_3 \to \mathbf{r}_3 + 2\mathbf{r}_2$, respectively.

---

**Definition**   A matrix obtained by performing an elementary row operation on an identity matrix is an **elementary matrix**.

---

The elementary row operation that is performed to obtain an elementary matrix from an identity matrix is called the elementary row operation *associated with* that elementary matrix.

We now demonstrate the most important property of elementary matrices. Below, we show the effect of multiplying the matrix

$$\mathbf{A} = \begin{pmatrix} 1 & 2 & 3 & 4 \\ 5 & 6 & 7 & 8 \\ 9 & 10 & 11 & 12 \end{pmatrix}$$

on the left by each of the above elementary matrices. Notice that in each case, the resulting matrix is precisely the matrix that is obtained when the row operation associated with the elementary matrix is performed on $\mathbf{A}$.

$$\underset{\substack{\text{elementary matrix} \\ \text{associated with} \\ \mathbf{r}_1 \leftrightarrow \mathbf{r}_2}}{\begin{pmatrix} 0 & 1 & 0 \\ 1 & 0 & 0 \\ 0 & 0 & 1 \end{pmatrix}} \underset{\mathbf{A}}{\begin{pmatrix} 1 & 2 & 3 & 4 \\ 5 & 6 & 7 & 8 \\ 9 & 10 & 11 & 12 \end{pmatrix}} = \underset{\substack{\text{matrix obtained when} \\ \mathbf{r}_1 \leftrightarrow \mathbf{r}_2 \\ \text{is performed on } \mathbf{A}}}{\begin{pmatrix} 5 & 6 & 7 & 8 \\ 1 & 2 & 3 & 4 \\ 9 & 10 & 11 & 12 \end{pmatrix}}$$

$$\underset{\substack{\text{elementary matrix} \\ \text{associated with} \\ \mathbf{r}_2 \to 5\mathbf{r}_2}}{\begin{pmatrix} 1 & 0 & 0 \\ 0 & 5 & 0 \\ 0 & 0 & 1 \end{pmatrix}} \underset{\mathbf{A}}{\begin{pmatrix} 1 & 2 & 3 & 4 \\ 5 & 6 & 7 & 8 \\ 9 & 10 & 11 & 12 \end{pmatrix}} = \underset{\substack{\text{matrix obtained when} \\ \mathbf{r}_2 \to 5\mathbf{r}_2 \\ \text{is performed on } \mathbf{A}}}{\begin{pmatrix} 1 & 2 & 3 & 4 \\ 25 & 30 & 35 & 40 \\ 9 & 10 & 11 & 12 \end{pmatrix}}$$

$$\underset{\substack{\text{elementary matrix} \\ \text{associated with} \\ \mathbf{r}_3 \to \mathbf{r}_3 + 2\mathbf{r}_2}}{\begin{pmatrix} 1 & 0 & 0 \\ 0 & 1 & 0 \\ 0 & 2 & 1 \end{pmatrix}} \underset{\mathbf{A}}{\begin{pmatrix} 1 & 2 & 3 & 4 \\ 5 & 6 & 7 & 8 \\ 9 & 10 & 11 & 12 \end{pmatrix}} = \underset{\substack{\text{matrix obtained when} \\ \mathbf{r}_3 \to \mathbf{r}_3 + 2\mathbf{r}_2 \\ \text{is performed on } \mathbf{A}}}{\begin{pmatrix} 1 & 2 & 3 & 4 \\ 5 & 6 & 7 & 8 \\ 19 & 22 & 25 & 28 \end{pmatrix}}$$

There is nothing special about the above elementary matrices, or about the above matrix $\mathbf{A}$. In the next exercise, you will find that other elementary matrices behave similarly.

**Exercise 4.6**   Let $\mathbf{A} = \begin{pmatrix} 1 & 2 & 3 \\ 3 & 2 & 1 \end{pmatrix}$ and $\mathbf{B} = \begin{pmatrix} 1 & 2 \\ 3 & 4 \\ 5 & 6 \\ 7 & 8 \end{pmatrix}$.

(a) Write down the $2 \times 2$ elementary matrix associated with the elementary row operation $\mathbf{r}_1 \to 5\mathbf{r}_1$.

This elementary matrix is the one obtained when $\mathbf{r}_1 \to 5\mathbf{r}_1$ is performed on the $2 \times 2$ identity matrix.

Multiply $\mathbf{A}$ on the left by this elementary matrix, and check that the resulting matrix is the same as the matrix obtained when $\mathbf{r}_1 \to 5\mathbf{r}_1$ is performed on $\mathbf{A}$.

(b) Write down the $4 \times 4$ elementary matrix associated with the elementary row operation $\mathbf{r}_2 \to \mathbf{r}_2 + 3\mathbf{r}_4$.

Multiply $\mathbf{B}$ on the left by this elementary matrix, and check that the resulting matrix is the same as the matrix obtained when $\mathbf{r}_2 \to \mathbf{r}_2 + 3\mathbf{r}_4$ is performed on $\mathbf{B}$.

In general, we have the following theorem.

---

**Theorem 4.8**   Let $\mathbf{E}$ be an elementary matrix, and let $\mathbf{A}$ be any matrix with the same number of rows as $\mathbf{E}$. Then the product $\mathbf{EA}$ is the same as the matrix obtained when the elementary row operation associated with $\mathbf{E}$ is performed on $\mathbf{A}$.

We omit the proof.

$\mathbf{A}$ must have the same number of rows as $\mathbf{E}$ for the product $\mathbf{EA}$ to be defined.

---

Theorem 4.8 tells us that if we perform an elementary row operation on a matrix $\mathbf{A}$ with $m$ rows, then the resulting matrix is $\mathbf{EA}$, where $\mathbf{E}$ is the $m \times m$ elementary matrix associated with the row operation.

What happens if we perform a *sequence* of $k$ elementary row operations on a matrix $\mathbf{A}$ with $m$ rows? Let $\mathbf{E}_1, \mathbf{E}_2, \ldots, \mathbf{E}_k$ be the $m \times m$ elementary matrices associated with the row operations in the sequence, in the same order. The first row operation is performed on $\mathbf{A}$, producing the matrix $\mathbf{E}_1\mathbf{A}$; the second row operation is then performed on *this* matrix, producing the matrix $\mathbf{E}_2(\mathbf{E}_1\mathbf{A}) = \mathbf{E}_2\mathbf{E}_1\mathbf{A}$; and so on. After the whole sequence of $k$ row operations has been performed, the resulting matrix is $\mathbf{E}_k\mathbf{E}_{k-1}\cdots\mathbf{E}_2\mathbf{E}_1\mathbf{A}$.

The order of the elementary matrices in the matrix product is the *reverse* of the order in which their associated row operations are performed.

This fact will be useful later, and we record it as a corollary to Theorem 4.8.

---

**Corollary to Theorem 4.8**   Let $\mathbf{E}_1, \mathbf{E}_2, \ldots, \mathbf{E}_k$ be the $m \times m$ elementary matrices associated with a sequence of $k$ elementary row operations carried out on a matrix $\mathbf{A}$ with $m$ rows, in the same order. Then, after the sequence of row operations has been performed, the resulting matrix is

$$\mathbf{E}_k\mathbf{E}_{k-1}\cdots\mathbf{E}_2\mathbf{E}_1\mathbf{A}.$$

---

For example, earlier we performed the sequence of row operations

$$\mathbf{r}_2 \to \mathbf{r}_2 - 2\mathbf{r}_1, \quad \mathbf{r}_2 \to \tfrac{1}{3}\mathbf{r}_2, \quad \mathbf{r}_1 \to \mathbf{r}_1 - 3\mathbf{r}_2,$$

on the matrix $\begin{pmatrix} 1 & 3 \\ 2 & 9 \end{pmatrix}$, producing the matrix $\begin{pmatrix} 1 & 0 \\ 0 & 1 \end{pmatrix}$.

By the above corollary,

$$\begin{pmatrix} 1 & 0 \\ 0 & 1 \end{pmatrix} = \begin{pmatrix} 1 & -3 \\ 0 & 1 \end{pmatrix} \begin{pmatrix} 1 & 0 \\ 0 & \frac{1}{3} \end{pmatrix} \begin{pmatrix} 1 & 0 \\ -2 & 1 \end{pmatrix} \begin{pmatrix} 1 & 3 \\ 2 & 9 \end{pmatrix}.$$

You should check this by evaluating the product on the right-hand side.

We now explore some other useful connections between elementary row operations and elementary matrices. We begin by introducing a further property of elementary row operations.

In the following example, the second elementary row operation undoes the effect of the first.

$$\mathbf{r}_1$$
$$\mathbf{r}_2$$
$$\begin{pmatrix} 1 & 2 & 3 \\ 4 & 5 & 6 \end{pmatrix}$$

$$\mathbf{r}_2 \to \mathbf{r}_2 + 3\mathbf{r}_1 \qquad \begin{pmatrix} 1 & 2 & 3 \\ 7 & 11 & 15 \end{pmatrix}$$

$$\mathbf{r}_2 \to \mathbf{r}_2 - 3\mathbf{r}_1 \qquad \begin{pmatrix} 1 & 2 & 3 \\ 4 & 5 & 6 \end{pmatrix}$$

In fact, given any elementary row operation, it is easy to write down an *inverse* elementary row operation that undoes the effect of the first, as summarised in the following table.

| Elementary row operation | Inverse elementary row operation |
| --- | --- |
| $\mathbf{r}_i \leftrightarrow \mathbf{r}_j$ | $\mathbf{r}_i \leftrightarrow \mathbf{r}_j$ |
| $\mathbf{r}_i \to c\,\mathbf{r}_i \quad (c \neq 0)$ | $\mathbf{r}_i \to (1/c)\,\mathbf{r}_i$ |
| $\mathbf{r}_i \to \mathbf{r}_i + c\,\mathbf{r}_j$ | $\mathbf{r}_i \to \mathbf{r}_i - c\,\mathbf{r}_j$ |

**Exercise 4.7**   Write down the inverse of each of the following elementary row operations. Check your answer in each case by carrying out the sequence of two row operations on the matrix $\begin{pmatrix} 1 & 2 & 3 \\ 4 & 5 & 6 \end{pmatrix}$.

(a)  $\mathbf{r}_1 \to \mathbf{r}_1 - 2\mathbf{r}_2$      (b)  $\mathbf{r}_1 \leftrightarrow \mathbf{r}_2$      (c)  $\mathbf{r}_2 \to -3\mathbf{r}_2$

Note from the table that if two elementary row operations are such that the second is the inverse of the first, then the first is the inverse of the second—so it makes sense to say that they are *inverses of each other*, or that they form an *inverse pair*. For example, the inverse of $\mathbf{r}_2 \to \mathbf{r}_2 + 3\mathbf{r}_1$ is $\mathbf{r}_2 \to \mathbf{r}_2 - 3\mathbf{r}_1$, and the inverse of $\mathbf{r}_2 \to \mathbf{r}_2 - 3\mathbf{r}_1$ is $\mathbf{r}_2 \to \mathbf{r}_2 - (-3)\mathbf{r}_1$, that is, $\mathbf{r}_2 \to \mathbf{r}_2 + 3\mathbf{r}_1$. So $\mathbf{r}_2 \to \mathbf{r}_2 + 3\mathbf{r}_1$ and $\mathbf{r}_2 \to \mathbf{r}_2 - 3\mathbf{r}_1$ are inverses of each other.

Now consider the following pair of $2 \times 2$ elementary matrices associated with the inverse pair of elementary row operations $\mathbf{r}_2 \to \mathbf{r}_2 + 3\mathbf{r}_1$ and $\mathbf{r}_2 \to \mathbf{r}_2 - 3\mathbf{r}_1$:

$$\begin{pmatrix} 1 & 0 \\ 3 & 1 \end{pmatrix}, \quad \begin{pmatrix} 1 & 0 \\ -3 & 1 \end{pmatrix}.$$

These two matrices are themselves inverses of each other, as we can easily check:

$$\begin{pmatrix} 1 & 0 \\ 3 & 1 \end{pmatrix} \begin{pmatrix} 1 & 0 \\ -3 & 1 \end{pmatrix} = \begin{pmatrix} 1 & 0 \\ 0 & 1 \end{pmatrix}$$

and

$$\begin{pmatrix} 1 & 0 \\ -3 & 1 \end{pmatrix} \begin{pmatrix} 1 & 0 \\ 3 & 1 \end{pmatrix} = \begin{pmatrix} 1 & 0 \\ 0 & 1 \end{pmatrix}.$$

This connection between inverse pairs of elementary row operations and inverse pairs of elementary matrices holds in general.

---

**Theorem 4.9**   Let $\mathbf{E}_1$ and $\mathbf{E}_2$ be elementary matrices of the same size whose associated elementary row operations are inverses of each other. Then $\mathbf{E}_1$ and $\mathbf{E}_2$ are inverses of each other.

---

**Proof**   In this proof we refer to the row operations associated with $\mathbf{E}_1$ and $\mathbf{E}_2$ as row operation 1 and row operation 2, respectively.

By the corollary to Theorem 4.8, $\mathbf{E}_2\mathbf{E}_1\mathbf{I}$ is the matrix produced when row operations 1 and 2 are performed, in that order, on $\mathbf{I}$. Similarly, $\mathbf{E}_1\mathbf{E}_2\mathbf{I}$ is the matrix produced when row operations 2 and 1 are performed, in that order, on $\mathbf{I}$. But each of these two row operations undoes the effect of the other, so $\mathbf{E}_2\mathbf{E}_1\mathbf{I} = \mathbf{I}$ and $\mathbf{E}_1\mathbf{E}_2\mathbf{I} = \mathbf{I}$; that is, $\mathbf{E}_2\mathbf{E}_1 = \mathbf{I}$ and $\mathbf{E}_1\mathbf{E}_2 = \mathbf{I}$. Thus $\mathbf{E}_1$ and $\mathbf{E}_2$ are inverses of each other.   ■

Theorem 4.9 has the following corollary.

---

**Corollary to Theorem 4.9**   Every elementary matrix is invertible, and its inverse is also an elementary matrix.

---

**Proof**   Let $\mathbf{E}$ be an elementary matrix. Then $\mathbf{E}$ has an associated elementary row operation. This associated elementary row operation has an inverse operation, and the elementary matrix of the same size as $\mathbf{E}$ associated with this inverse operation is the inverse of $\mathbf{E}$, by Theorem 4.9.   ■

**Exercise 4.8**   Use the method suggested by the proof of the above corollary to find the inverse of the elementary matrix $\begin{pmatrix} 2 & 0 & 0 \\ 0 & 1 & 0 \\ 0 & 0 & 1 \end{pmatrix}$.

# 4.5  Proof of the Invertibility Theorem

We are now ready to prove the Invertibility Theorem, using elementary matrices and their properties. We first remind you of the theorem.

---

**Theorem 4.5  Invertibility Theorem**

(a)  A square matrix is invertible if and only if its row-reduced form is $\mathbf{I}$.

(b)  Any sequence of elementary row operations that transforms a matrix $\mathbf{A}$ to $\mathbf{I}$ also transforms $\mathbf{I}$ to $\mathbf{A}^{-1}$.

---

**Proof**    Let $\mathbf{A}$ be an $n \times n$ matrix, and let the row-reduced form of $\mathbf{A}$ be $\mathbf{U}$. Let $\mathbf{E}_1, \mathbf{E}_2, \ldots, \mathbf{E}_k$ be the $n \times n$ elementary matrices associated with a sequence of $k$ elementary row operations that transforms $\mathbf{A}$ to $\mathbf{U}$, in the same order. Then, by the corollary to Theorem 4.8,

$$\mathbf{U} = \mathbf{BA},$$

where $\mathbf{B} = \mathbf{E}_k \mathbf{E}_{k-1} \cdots \mathbf{E}_2 \mathbf{E}_1$. Now $\mathbf{B}$ is invertible—since every elementary matrix is invertible (by the corollary to Theorem 4.9), and a product of invertible matrices is invertible (by Theorem 4.3).

(a) First we show that if $\mathbf{A}$ is invertible, then $\mathbf{U} = \mathbf{I}$.

This is the 'only if' part of the proof.

Suppose that $\mathbf{A}$ is invertible. Then $\mathbf{U}$ is a product of invertible matrices ($\mathbf{B}$ and $\mathbf{A}$); hence $\mathbf{U}$ is invertible.

Therefore $\mathbf{U}$ does not have a zero row (since, by Theorem 4.2, a square matrix with a zero row is not invertible), so it has a leading 1 in each of its $n$ rows. Each of these $n$ leading 1s lies in a different column; so, since $\mathbf{U}$ has only $n$ columns, each column must contain a leading 1. Thus the leading 1 in the top row must lie in the left-most position, and the leading 1 in each subsequent row must lie just one position to the right of the leading 1 in the row immediately above. All the entries above and below these leading 1s are 0s. Hence $\mathbf{U} = \mathbf{I}$.

Next, we show that if $\mathbf{U} = \mathbf{I}$, then $\mathbf{A}$ is invertible.

This is the 'if' part of the proof.

Suppose that $\mathbf{U} = \mathbf{I}$. Then

$$\mathbf{I} = \mathbf{BA}. \tag{4.1}$$

Multiplying both sides of equation (4.1) on the left by $\mathbf{B}^{-1}$ yields

$$\mathbf{B}^{-1}\mathbf{I} = \mathbf{B}^{-1}\mathbf{BA},$$

that is,

$$\mathbf{B}^{-1} = \mathbf{A}.$$

Multiplying both sides of *this* equation on the right by $\mathbf{B}$ yields

$$\mathbf{B}^{-1}\mathbf{B} = \mathbf{AB},$$

that is,

$$\mathbf{I} = \mathbf{AB}. \tag{4.2}$$

Equations (4.1) and (4.2) together tell us that $\mathbf{A}$ is invertible, and that $\mathbf{A}^{-1} = \mathbf{B}$.

(b) It follows from the proof of part (a) that if $\mathbf{U} = \mathbf{I}$, then $\mathbf{A}$ is invertible and $\mathbf{A}^{-1} = \mathbf{B}$; that is, $\mathbf{A}^{-1} = \mathbf{E}_k \mathbf{E}_{k-1} \cdots \mathbf{E}_2 \mathbf{E}_1$.

This equation can be written as

$$\mathbf{A}^{-1} = \mathbf{E}_k \mathbf{E}_{k-1} \cdots \mathbf{E}_2 \mathbf{E}_1 \mathbf{I},$$

which tells us that $\mathbf{A}^{-1}$ is the matrix produced by performing on $\mathbf{I}$ the sequence of row operations associated with $\mathbf{E}_1, \mathbf{E}_2, \ldots, \mathbf{E}_k$. ∎

# Further exercises

**Exercise 4.9**  Let $\mathbf{A}$ be an invertible matrix. Prove that if $k$ is a non-zero number, then $k\mathbf{A}$ is invertible, with $(k\mathbf{A})^{-1} = (1/k)\mathbf{A}^{-1}$.

**Exercise 4.10** Use Strategy 4.1 to determine whether or not each of the following matrices is invertible, and find the inverse if it exists.

(a) $\begin{pmatrix} 2 & 3 \\ 3 & 5 \end{pmatrix}$     (b) $\begin{pmatrix} -2 & 4 \\ 3 & -6 \end{pmatrix}$     (c) $\begin{pmatrix} 1 & 2 & 4 \\ -2 & -1 & 1 \\ 1 & 1 & 1 \end{pmatrix}$

(d) $\begin{pmatrix} 1 & 4 & 1 \\ 1 & 6 & 3 \\ 2 & 3 & 0 \end{pmatrix}$     (e) $\begin{pmatrix} 1 & 0 & 0 & 3 \\ 0 & 1 & 2 & 0 \\ 0 & -1 & -1 & 0 \\ -1 & 0 & 0 & -2 \end{pmatrix}$

**Exercise 4.11**   Use your answers to Exercise 4.10(a) and (d) to solve the following systems of linear equations.

(a) $\begin{cases} 2x + 3y = 3 \\ 3x + 5y = 4 \end{cases}$     (b) $\begin{cases} x_1 + 4x_2 + x_3 = 4 \\ x_1 + 6x_2 + 3x_3 = 6 \\ 2x_1 + 3x_2 \quad\quad = 9 \end{cases}$

**Exercise 4.12**

(a) Show that a square matrix is invertible if and only if it can be expressed as a product of elementary matrices.

   Hint: Use ideas from the proof of the Invertibility Theorem.

(b) Express the matrix in Exercise 4.10(a) as a product of elementary matrices.

# 5   Determinants

After working through this section, you should be able to:

(a) understand the term *determinant* of a square matrix;

(b) evaluate the determinant of a $2 \times 2$ or $3 \times 3$ matrix;

(c) *expand along the top row* to calculate the determinant of a matrix;

(d) determine whether or not a given $2 \times 2$ matrix is invertible, and if it is, find its inverse;

(e) use determinants to check whether or not a matrix is invertible.

## 5.1   Systems of linear equations and determinants

Determinants arise naturally in the study of systems of simultaneous linear equations. If a unique solution exists for a system of $n$ linear equations in $n$ unknowns, then this solution can be found by evaluating determinants, a method known as *Cramer's Rule*.

### Determinant of a $2 \times 2$ matrix

We start by looking at a system of two equations in two unknowns:

$$\begin{cases} a_1 x + b_1 y = c_1 \\ a_2 x + b_2 y = c_2 \end{cases} \quad \text{or} \quad \begin{pmatrix} a_1 & b_1 \\ a_2 & b_2 \end{pmatrix}\begin{pmatrix} x \\ y \end{pmatrix} = \begin{pmatrix} c_1 \\ c_2 \end{pmatrix}.$$

The coefficients of the system are real numbers.

Using Gauss–Jordan elimination, we find the solution to be

$$x = \frac{c_1 b_2 - b_1 c_2}{a_1 b_2 - b_1 a_2}, \quad y = \frac{a_1 c_2 - c_1 a_2}{a_1 b_2 - b_1 a_2}, \tag{5.1}$$

You can check this solution by substitution.

provided that $a_1 b_2 - b_1 a_2$ is not zero. We call the expression $a_1 b_2 - b_1 a_2$ the *determinant* of the coefficient matrix. Each term in this expression contains the letters $a$ and $b$, and the subscripts 1 and 2, in some order.

The definition we give for the determinant of a $2 \times 2$ matrix is in a form that is easy to remember.

You might find it helpful to remember the following scheme:

---

**Definition**   The **determinant** of a $2 \times 2$ matrix

$$\mathbf{A} = \begin{pmatrix} a & b \\ c & d \end{pmatrix}$$

is

$$\det \mathbf{A} = \begin{vmatrix} a & b \\ c & d \end{vmatrix} = ad - bc.$$

---

We use vertical bars '| ... |' around the matrix entries, in place of the round brackets, to denote the determinant.

Some texts use the notation $|\mathbf{A}|$ for $\det \mathbf{A}$.

For example, let $\mathbf{A} = \begin{pmatrix} 1 & 2 \\ 3 & 4 \end{pmatrix}$; then

$$\det \mathbf{A} = \begin{vmatrix} 1 & 2 \\ 3 & 4 \end{vmatrix} = (1 \times 4) - (2 \times 3) = -2.$$

**Exercise 5.1**   Evaluate the determinant of each of the following matrices.

(a) $\begin{pmatrix} 5 & 1 \\ 4 & 2 \end{pmatrix}$     (b) $\begin{pmatrix} 10 & -4 \\ -5 & 2 \end{pmatrix}$     (c) $\begin{pmatrix} 7 & 3 \\ 17 & 2 \end{pmatrix}$

Notice that the numerators of the solutions for $x$ and $y$ in (5.1) can also be written as determinants:

$$c_1 b_2 - b_1 c_2 = \begin{vmatrix} c_1 & b_1 \\ c_2 & b_2 \end{vmatrix} \quad \text{and} \quad a_1 c_2 - c_1 a_2 = \begin{vmatrix} a_1 & c_1 \\ a_2 & c_2 \end{vmatrix}.$$

We could write the solutions as

$$x = \frac{\begin{vmatrix} c_1 & b_1 \\ c_2 & b_2 \end{vmatrix}}{\begin{vmatrix} a_1 & b_1 \\ a_2 & b_2 \end{vmatrix}}, \quad y = \frac{\begin{vmatrix} a_1 & c_1 \\ a_2 & c_2 \end{vmatrix}}{\begin{vmatrix} a_1 & b_1 \\ a_2 & b_2 \end{vmatrix}}.$$

A $2 \times 2$ matrix is invertible if and only if its determinant is non-zero. For an invertible $2 \times 2$ matrix, there is a quick way to find the inverse using the determinant.

We shall prove this statement in Subsection 5.4.

---

**Strategy 5.1**   To find the inverse of a $2 \times 2$ matrix

$$\mathbf{A} = \begin{pmatrix} a & b \\ c & d \end{pmatrix}$$

with $\det \mathbf{A} = ad - bc \neq 0$.

1.   Interchange the diagonal entries.

2.   Multiply the non-diagonal entries by $-1$.

3.   Divide by the determinant,

giving

$$\mathbf{A}^{-1} = \frac{1}{ad - bc} \begin{pmatrix} d & -b \\ -c & a \end{pmatrix}.$$

---

**Exercise 5.2**   Determine whether or not each of the following matrices is invertible, and find the inverse if it exists.

(a) $\begin{pmatrix} 4 & 2 \\ 5 & 6 \end{pmatrix}$    (b) $\begin{pmatrix} 1 & 1 \\ -1 & 1 \end{pmatrix}$    (c) $\begin{pmatrix} 1 & -1 \\ -1 & 1 \end{pmatrix}$

*Remark*   There is also a geometric interpretation of the determinant. For example, the parallelogram with vertices $(0,0)$, $(2,1)$, $(1,3)$ and $(3,4)$ has area 5. Now, since one of the vertices is at the origin, the position vectors $(2,1)$ and $(1,3)$ determine the parallelogram, and

$$\begin{vmatrix} 2 & 1 \\ 1 & 3 \end{vmatrix} = (2 \times 3) - (1 \times 1) = 5.$$

In general, let $(a,b)$ and $(c,d)$ be two position vectors. Then the determinant

$$\begin{vmatrix} a & b \\ c & d \end{vmatrix}$$

gives the area of the parallelogram with adjacent sides given by these position vectors.

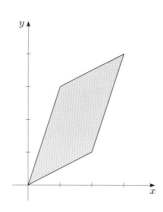

## Determinant of a $3 \times 3$ matrix

We now consider the following system of three linear equations in three unknowns:

$$\begin{cases} a_1 x + b_1 y + c_1 z = d_1 \\ a_2 x + b_2 y + c_2 z = d_2 \\ a_3 x + b_3 y + c_3 z = d_3 \end{cases} \quad \text{or} \quad \begin{pmatrix} a_1 & b_1 & c_1 \\ a_2 & b_2 & c_2 \\ a_3 & b_3 & c_3 \end{pmatrix} \begin{pmatrix} x \\ y \\ z \end{pmatrix} = \begin{pmatrix} d_1 \\ d_2 \\ d_3 \end{pmatrix}.$$

Again we can find the solution, if one exists, using Gauss–Jordan elimination. The expressions for $x$, $y$ and $z$ all have the same denominator:

$$a_1 b_2 c_3 - a_1 c_2 b_3 - b_1 a_2 c_3 + b_1 c_2 a_3 + c_1 a_2 b_3 - c_1 b_2 a_3.$$

You are not expected to find these expressions; they serve only to motivate the definition of the determinant.

This is the *determinant* of the $3 \times 3$ coefficient matrix. Notice that each term in the expression contains the letters $a$, $b$ and $c$, and the subscripts 1, 2 and 3, in some order.

The definition we give for the determinant of a $3 \times 3$ matrix is expressed in terms of three $2 \times 2$ determinants. This is the easiest way to remember the definition.

---

**Definition**   The **determinant** of a $3 \times 3$ matrix

$$\mathbf{A} = \begin{pmatrix} a_1 & b_1 & c_1 \\ a_2 & b_2 & c_2 \\ a_3 & b_3 & c_3 \end{pmatrix}$$

is

$$\det \mathbf{A} = a_1 \begin{vmatrix} b_2 & c_2 \\ b_3 & c_3 \end{vmatrix} - b_1 \begin{vmatrix} a_2 & c_2 \\ a_3 & c_3 \end{vmatrix} + c_1 \begin{vmatrix} a_2 & b_2 \\ a_3 & b_3 \end{vmatrix}.$$

---

Notice the minus sign before the second term on the right-hand side.

**Example 5.1**   Evaluate the determinant of each of the following $3 \times 3$ matrices.

(a) $\begin{pmatrix} 1 & 2 & 1 \\ 3 & 1 & -1 \\ -2 & 1 & 1 \end{pmatrix}$    (b) $\begin{pmatrix} 4 & 0 & 1 \\ 0 & -1 & 2 \\ 2 & 1 & 3 \end{pmatrix}$

## Solution

(a) $\begin{vmatrix} 1 & 2 & 1 \\ 3 & 1 & -1 \\ -2 & 1 & 1 \end{vmatrix} = 1 \begin{vmatrix} 1 & -1 \\ 1 & 1 \end{vmatrix} - 2 \begin{vmatrix} 3 & -1 \\ -2 & 1 \end{vmatrix} + 1 \begin{vmatrix} 3 & 1 \\ -2 & 1 \end{vmatrix}$

$$= 1\left((1 \times 1) - (-1 \times 1)\right) - 2\left((3 \times 1) - (-1 \times -2)\right)$$
$$+ 1\left((3 \times 1) - (1 \times -2)\right)$$
$$= 5$$

(b) $\begin{vmatrix} 4 & 0 & 1 \\ 0 & -1 & 2 \\ 2 & 1 & 3 \end{vmatrix} = 4 \begin{vmatrix} -1 & 2 \\ 1 & 3 \end{vmatrix} - 0 \begin{vmatrix} 0 & 2 \\ 2 & 3 \end{vmatrix} + 1 \begin{vmatrix} 0 & -1 \\ 2 & 1 \end{vmatrix}$

$$= 4\left((-1 \times 3) - (2 \times 1)\right) - 0 + 1\left((0 \times 1) - (-1 \times 2)\right)$$
$$= -18 \quad \blacksquare$$

**Exercise 5.3**   Evaluate the determinant of each of the following $3 \times 3$ matrices.

(a) $\begin{pmatrix} 3 & 2 & 1 \\ 4 & 0 & -1 \\ 0 & -1 & 1 \end{pmatrix}$     (b) $\begin{pmatrix} 2 & 10 & 0 \\ 3 & -1 & 2 \\ 5 & 9 & 2 \end{pmatrix}$

Determinants of larger matrices ($4 \times 4$, and so on) will be defined similarly. Note that determinants are defined only for square matrices.

# 5.2  Evaluating determinants

We have seen that although the determinant of a $2 \times 2$ matrix is simple to evaluate, the determinant of a $3 \times 3$ matrix is quite complicated. Determinants of larger matrices become increasingly more complicated as the size of the matrix increases. In this subsection we develop a strategy for evaluating determinants by expressing them eventually in terms of determinants of $2 \times 2$ matrices, as with the definition of the determinant of a $3 \times 3$ matrix above.

*You will mainly be finding determinants of matrices of size $2 \times 2$ and $3 \times 3$.*

## Cofactors

We can express the determinant of a $3 \times 3$ matrix $\mathbf{A} = (a_{ij})$ conveniently as

$$\det \mathbf{A} = a_{11}A_{11} + a_{12}A_{12} + a_{13}A_{13}.$$

The elements $A_{11}$, $A_{12}$ and $A_{13}$ in this expression are called the *cofactors* of the elements $a_{11}$, $a_{12}$ and $a_{13}$, respectively. We can see from the definition of the determinant that these cofactors are themselves determinants with a $+$ or $-$ sign attached. $A_{1j}$ is $+$ or $-$ the determinant of a submatrix of $\mathbf{A}$ formed by covering up the top row and one column of $\mathbf{A}$—namely, the row and column containing the element $a_{1j}$. Thus

*A submatrix is a matrix formed from another matrix with some of the rows and/or columns removed.*

$$A_{11} = \begin{vmatrix} \mathbf{a_{11}} & a_{12} & a_{13} \\ a_{21} & a_{22} & a_{23} \\ a_{31} & a_{32} & a_{33} \end{vmatrix} = \begin{vmatrix} a_{22} & a_{23} \\ a_{32} & a_{33} \end{vmatrix},$$

$$A_{12} = (-1)\begin{vmatrix} a_{11} & \mathbf{a_{12}} & a_{13} \\ a_{21} & a_{22} & a_{23} \\ a_{31} & a_{32} & a_{33} \end{vmatrix} = (-1)\begin{vmatrix} a_{21} & a_{23} \\ a_{31} & a_{33} \end{vmatrix}$$

*Notice the factor $(-1)$ in $A_{12}$.*

and

$$A_{13} = \begin{vmatrix} a_{11} & a_{12} & \mathbf{a_{13}} \\ a_{21} & a_{22} & a_{23} \\ a_{31} & a_{32} & \mathbf{a_{33}} \end{vmatrix} = \begin{vmatrix} a_{21} & a_{22} \\ a_{31} & a_{32} \end{vmatrix}.$$

In fact, there is a *cofactor* associated with each entry of any square matrix.

---

**Definition**  Let $\mathbf{A} = (a_{ij})$ be an $n \times n$ matrix. The **cofactor** $A_{ij}$ associated with the entry $a_{ij}$ is

$$A_{ij} = (-1)^{i+j} \det \mathbf{A}_{ij},$$

where $\mathbf{A}_{ij}$ is the $(n-1) \times (n-1)$ submatrix of $\mathbf{A}$ resulting when the $i$th row and $j$th column (the row and column containing the entry $a_{ij}$) are covered up.

---

*Remember the minus sign attached to alternate terms.*

For example, the cofactor $A_{23}$ of the $4 \times 4$ matrix $\mathbf{A} = (a_{ij})$ is

$$A_{23} = (-1) \begin{vmatrix} a_{11} & a_{12} & a_{14} \\ a_{31} & a_{32} & a_{34} \\ a_{41} & a_{42} & a_{44} \end{vmatrix}.$$

**Exercise 5.4**  Write down expressions for the cofactors $A_{13}$ and $A_{45}$ of the matrix

$$\mathbf{A} = \begin{pmatrix} 1 & 2 & 3 & 4 & 5 \\ 2 & 3 & 4 & 5 & 1 \\ 3 & 4 & 5 & 1 & 2 \\ 4 & 5 & 1 & 2 & 3 \\ 5 & 1 & 2 & 3 & 4 \end{pmatrix}.$$

*Do not attempt to evaluate these expressions!*

## Determinant of an $n \times n$ matrix

You have seen that we can use cofactors to evaluate the determinant of a $3 \times 3$ matrix. Determinants of larger matrices can be evaluated in a similar way.

---

**Definition**    The **determinant** of an $n \times n$ matrix $\mathbf{A} = (a_{ij})$ is

$$\det \mathbf{A} = \begin{vmatrix} a_{11} & a_{12} & \cdots & a_{1n} \\ a_{21} & a_{22} & \cdots & a_{2n} \\ \vdots & \vdots & & \vdots \\ a_{n1} & a_{n2} & \cdots & a_{nn} \end{vmatrix}$$

$$= a_{11}A_{11} + a_{12}A_{12} + \cdots + a_{1n}A_{1n}.$$

---

The determinant of a matrix is a complicated string of terms. The definition above collects the terms into manageable expressions using the cofactors of the entries of the top row; when we write the determinant in this way, we say that we are *expanding along the top row*.

*There are alternative expansions for the determinant of a square matrix that collect the terms in different ways—however, the resulting value for the determinant is always the same.*

We are now in a position to evaluate the determinant of any square matrix using the following strategy.

---

**Strategy 5.2**   To evaluate the determinant of an $n \times n$ matrix.

1. Expand along the top row to express the $n \times n$ determinant in terms of $n$ determinants of size $(n-1) \times (n-1)$.

2. Expand along the top row of each of the resulting determinants.

3. Repeatedly apply step 2 until the only determinants in the expression are of size $2 \times 2$.

4. Evaluate the final expression.

---

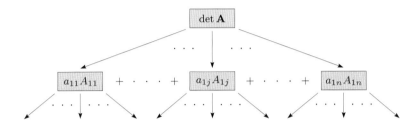

We illustrate Strategy 5.2 with an example.

**Example 5.2**   Evaluate the determinant

$$\begin{vmatrix} 2 & 0 & 3 & 5 \\ 0 & 4 & -1 & 0 \\ 1 & 0 & 0 & 1 \\ 0 & 2 & 1 & 1 \end{vmatrix}.$$

**Solution**   We apply Strategy 5.2.

$$\begin{vmatrix} 2 & 0 & 3 & 5 \\ 0 & 4 & -1 & 0 \\ 1 & 0 & 0 & 1 \\ 0 & 2 & 1 & 1 \end{vmatrix} = 2\begin{vmatrix} 4 & -1 & 0 \\ 0 & 0 & 1 \\ 2 & 1 & 1 \end{vmatrix} - 0 + 3\begin{vmatrix} 0 & 4 & 0 \\ 1 & 0 & 1 \\ 0 & 2 & 1 \end{vmatrix} - 5\begin{vmatrix} 0 & 4 & -1 \\ 1 & 0 & 0 \\ 0 & 2 & 1 \end{vmatrix}$$

$$= 2\left(4\begin{vmatrix} 0 & 1 \\ 1 & 1 \end{vmatrix} - (-1)\begin{vmatrix} 0 & 1 \\ 2 & 1 \end{vmatrix} + 0\right)$$

$$+ 3\left(0 - 4\begin{vmatrix} 1 & 1 \\ 0 & 1 \end{vmatrix} + 0\right)$$

$$- 5\left(0 - 4\begin{vmatrix} 1 & 0 \\ 0 & 1 \end{vmatrix} + (-1)\begin{vmatrix} 1 & 0 \\ 0 & 2 \end{vmatrix}\right)$$

$$= 2(-4 - 2) + 3(-4) - 5(-4 - 2)$$

$$= -12 - 12 + 30$$

$$= 6. \quad \blacksquare$$

**Exercise 5.5**   Evaluate the determinant

$$\begin{vmatrix} 0 & 2 & 1 & -1 \\ -3 & 0 & 0 & -1 \\ 1 & 0 & 1 & 0 \\ 0 & 4 & 2 & 0 \end{vmatrix}.$$

# 5.3 Properties of determinants

Suppose that $\mathbf{A}$ and $\mathbf{B}$ are two square matrices of the same size. Are there any relationships between $\det \mathbf{A}$, $\det \mathbf{B}$, $\det(\mathbf{A} + \mathbf{B})$ and $\det(\mathbf{AB})$?

**Exercise 5.6** Let $\mathbf{A} = \begin{pmatrix} -3 & 1 \\ 2 & -4 \end{pmatrix}$ and $\mathbf{B} = \begin{pmatrix} 1 & 1 \\ -2 & 5 \end{pmatrix}$.

Evaluate $\det \mathbf{A}$, $\det \mathbf{B}$, $\det(\mathbf{A} + \mathbf{B})$, $\det(\mathbf{AB})$ and $(\det \mathbf{A})(\det \mathbf{B})$. Comment on your results.

You should have found in the solution to Exercise 5.6 that there does not appear to be a simple relationship for the addition of determinants; that is, we cannot easily express $\det(\mathbf{A} + \mathbf{B})$ in terms of $\det \mathbf{A}$ and $\det \mathbf{B}$. However, the identity

$$\det(\mathbf{AB}) = (\det \mathbf{A})(\det \mathbf{B})$$

holds for all square matrices $\mathbf{A}$ and $\mathbf{B}$ of the same size. The simplicity of this result is somewhat surprising, given the complexity of the definitions of matrix multiplication and the determinant.

We collect together some results for determinants in the following theorem.

---

**Theorem 5.1** Let $\mathbf{A}$ and $\mathbf{B}$ be two square matrices of the same size. Then the following hold:

(a) $\det(\mathbf{AB}) = (\det \mathbf{A})(\det \mathbf{B})$;

(b) $\det \mathbf{I} = 1$;

(c) $\det \mathbf{A}^T = \det \mathbf{A}$.

We omit the proof.

---

## Elementary operations and determinants

Earlier, we saw that multiplication on the left by an *elementary matrix* has the same effect as applying the associated elementary row operation. Here, we use elementary matrices to prove some useful results about determinants.

Theorem 4.8

**Exercise 5.7** Evaluate the following determinants, where $k$ is any real number.

(a) $\begin{vmatrix} 0 & 1 & 0 \\ 1 & 0 & 0 \\ 0 & 0 & 1 \end{vmatrix}$
(b) $\begin{vmatrix} 1 & 0 & 0 & 0 \\ 0 & 1 & 0 & 0 \\ 0 & 0 & k & 0 \\ 0 & 0 & 0 & 1 \end{vmatrix}$
(c) $\begin{vmatrix} 1 & 0 \\ k & 1 \end{vmatrix}$

The results of Exercise 5.7 are special cases of the following theorem.

---

**Theorem 5.2** Let $\mathbf{E}$ be an elementary matrix, and let $k$ be a non-zero real number.

(a) If $\mathbf{E}$ results from interchanging two rows of $\mathbf{I}$, then $\det \mathbf{E} = -1$.

(b) If $\mathbf{E}$ results from multiplying a row of $\mathbf{I}$ by $k$, then $\det \mathbf{E} = k$.

(c) If $\mathbf{E}$ results from adding $k$ times one row of $\mathbf{I}$ to another row, then $\det \mathbf{E} = 1$.

We omit the proof.

---

Zeros in a matrix greatly simplify the calculation of the determinant. If an entire row of the matrix is zero, then all the terms vanish and the determinant is zero. Other matrices with zero determinant are also easy to recognise.

---

**Theorem 5.3**   Let $\mathbf{A}$ be a square matrix. Then $\det \mathbf{A} = 0$ if any of the following hold:

(a) $\mathbf{A}$ has an entire row (or column) of zeros;

(b) $\mathbf{A}$ has two equal rows (or columns);

(c) $\mathbf{A}$ has two proportional rows (or columns).

---

Two rows (or columns) of a matrix are *proportional* when one is a multiple of the other.

**Proof**   We prove the statements for rows. The results for columns follow, as Theorem 5.1(c) states that taking the transpose does not alter the determinant of a matrix.

(a) Each term in the expansion of the determinant of $\mathbf{A}$ contains one entry from each row and each column of $\mathbf{A}$. If an entire row of $\mathbf{A}$ is zero, then each term of the expansion contains at least one zero. The determinant of $\mathbf{A}$ is therefore equal to zero.

(b) If the $i$th and $j$th rows of the matrix $\mathbf{A}$ are equal, then $\mathbf{A}$ remains the same if these rows are interchanged. Let $\mathbf{E}$ be the elementary matrix obtained by interchanging the $i$th and $j$th rows of $\mathbf{I}$. Then $\mathbf{EA} = \mathbf{A}$. Using Theorems 5.1 and 5.2, we have

$$\det \mathbf{A} = \det(\mathbf{EA}) = (\det \mathbf{E})(\det \mathbf{A}) = -1 \times \det \mathbf{A}.$$

This implies that $\det \mathbf{A} = 0$, as required.

(c) Suppose that the $i$th row of $\mathbf{A}$ is equal to $k$ times the $j$th row. Let $\mathbf{E}$ be the elementary matrix obtained from $\mathbf{I}$ by multiplying the $i$th row by $1/k$. Then the $i$th and $j$th rows of the matrix $\mathbf{EA}$ are equal. The determinant of this matrix $\mathbf{EA}$ is zero, by (b) above. Using Theorem 5.1, we have

$$(\det \mathbf{E})(\det \mathbf{A}) = \det(\mathbf{EA}) = 0.$$

Now $\det \mathbf{E} = 1/k$, by Theorem 5.2. This implies that $\det \mathbf{A} = 0$, as required.   ∎

**Exercise 5.8**   Evaluate the determinant of the matrix

$$\mathbf{A} = \begin{pmatrix} 1 & -2 & 4 \\ 0 & 13 & 11 \\ -2 & 4 & -8 \end{pmatrix}.$$

The evaluation of the determinant can be significantly simplified if a row of the matrix contains some zeros, as the following example illustrates.

**Example 5.3**   Evaluate the determinant of the matrix

$$\mathbf{A} = \begin{pmatrix} 1 & 4 & 2 \\ 0 & 7 & 0 \\ 3 & 1 & 5 \end{pmatrix}.$$

**Solution** First notice that the second row of $\mathbf{A}$ has only one non-zero entry. We interchange the top two rows of $\mathbf{A}$, and apply Theorems 5.1 and 5.2, giving

$$\det \mathbf{A} = \begin{vmatrix} 1 & 4 & 2 \\ 0 & 7 & 0 \\ 3 & 1 & 5 \end{vmatrix} = (-1) \begin{vmatrix} 0 & 7 & 0 \\ 1 & 4 & 2 \\ 3 & 1 & 5 \end{vmatrix}.$$

We use Strategy 5.2 to evaluate this determinant:

$$\det \mathbf{A} = (-1) \left( 0 - 7 \begin{vmatrix} 1 & 2 \\ 3 & 5 \end{vmatrix} + 0 \right)$$

$$= 7((1 \times 5) - (2 \times 3))$$

$$= -7. \quad \blacksquare$$

The calculation has been simplified by interchanging rows, as there is only one non-zero term in this expansion.

**Exercise 5.9** Evaluate the determinant of the matrix

$$\mathbf{A} = \begin{pmatrix} 10 & 3 & -4 & 2 \\ 0 & 2 & 0 & 1 \\ 0 & 6 & 0 & 0 \\ -1 & 2 & 1 & 0 \end{pmatrix}.$$

# 5.4 Determinants and inverses of matrices

Earlier, we stated that the inverse of a $2 \times 2$ matrix $\mathbf{A}$ exists if and only if $\det \mathbf{A} \neq 0$. This extends to all square matrices.

---

**Theorem 5.4** A square matrix $\mathbf{A}$ is invertible if and only if $\det \mathbf{A} \neq 0$.

---

**Proof** Let $\mathbf{A}$ be an $n \times n$ matrix.

We begin by assuming that $\mathbf{A}$ is invertible.

Since $\mathbf{A}\mathbf{A}^{-1} = \mathbf{I}_n$, it follows from Theorem 5.1 that

$$(\det \mathbf{A})(\det \mathbf{A}^{-1}) = \det(\mathbf{A}\mathbf{A}^{-1}) = \det \mathbf{I}_n = 1.$$

Therefore neither $\det \mathbf{A}$ nor $\det \mathbf{A}^{-1}$ is 0.

We now assume that $\det \mathbf{A} \neq 0$. Let $\mathbf{E}_1, \ldots, \mathbf{E}_k$ be elementary matrices such that $\mathbf{E}_k \cdots \mathbf{E}_2 \mathbf{E}_1 \mathbf{A} = \mathbf{U}$ is a matrix in row-reduced form. Using Theorems 5.1 and 5.2 and the assumption that $\det \mathbf{A} \neq 0$, we have

$$\det \mathbf{U} = (\det \mathbf{E}_k) \cdots (\det \mathbf{E}_2)(\det \mathbf{E}_1)(\det \mathbf{A}) \neq 0.$$

Now this implies that $\mathbf{U}$ has no zero row, and therefore has a leading 1 in each of its $n$ rows. Hence $\mathbf{U} = \mathbf{I}_n$, and so, by the Invertibility Theorem, the matrix $\mathbf{A}$ is invertible, with

$$\mathbf{A}^{-1} = \mathbf{E}_k \cdots \mathbf{E}_2 \mathbf{E}_1. \quad \blacksquare$$

We saw in the proof of Theorem 5.4 above that if $\mathbf{A}$ is invertible, then $(\det \mathbf{A})(\det \mathbf{A}^{-1}) = 1$. This implies that

$$\det \mathbf{A}^{-1} = \frac{1}{\det \mathbf{A}}.$$

Until now, if we wanted to show that an $n \times n$ matrix $\mathbf{A}$ is invertible, we had to produce an $n \times n$ matrix $\mathbf{B}$ such that

$$\mathbf{AB} = \mathbf{I} \quad \text{and} \quad \mathbf{BA} = \mathbf{I}.$$

The next theorem shows that if one of these conditions holds, then the other holds automatically. Thus, if we want to show that an $n \times n$ matrix $\mathbf{A}$ is invertible, it is enough to produce an $n \times n$ matrix $\mathbf{B}$ satisfying *either* condition.

---

**Theorem 5.5**  Let $\mathbf{A}$ and $\mathbf{B}$ be square matrices of the same size. Then $\mathbf{AB} = \mathbf{I}$ if and only if $\mathbf{BA} = \mathbf{I}$.

---

**Proof**  We first assume that $\mathbf{AB} = \mathbf{I}$. Then by Theorem 5.1,

$$(\det \mathbf{A})(\det \mathbf{B}) = \det(\mathbf{AB}) = \det \mathbf{I} = 1.$$

This implies that

$$\det \mathbf{A} \neq 0 \quad \text{and} \quad \det \mathbf{B} \neq 0,$$

so, by Theorem 5.4, $\mathbf{A}$ and $\mathbf{B}$ are both invertible.

Now,

$$\mathbf{A}^{-1} = \mathbf{A}^{-1}\mathbf{I},$$

and we can write $\mathbf{I}$ as $\mathbf{AB}$, so

$$\mathbf{A}^{-1} = \mathbf{A}^{-1}(\mathbf{AB}) = (\mathbf{A}^{-1}\mathbf{A})\mathbf{B} = \mathbf{IB} = \mathbf{B},$$

and therefore

$$\mathbf{BA} = \mathbf{A}^{-1}\mathbf{A} = \mathbf{I},$$

as required.

The same argument, with the roles of $\mathbf{A}$ and $\mathbf{B}$ interchanged, proves the converse. ∎

We summarise the results on the invertibility of a matrix $\mathbf{A}$ as follows.

---

**Theorem 5.6  Summary Theorem**

Let $\mathbf{A}$ be an $n \times n$ matrix. Then the following statements are equivalent.

(a) $\mathbf{A}$ is invertible.

(b) $\det \mathbf{A} \neq 0$.

(c) The row-reduced form of $\mathbf{A}$ is $\mathbf{I}_n$.

(d) The system $\mathbf{Ax} = \mathbf{b}$ has precisely one solution for each $n \times 1$ matrix $\mathbf{b}$.

(e) The system $\mathbf{Ax} = \mathbf{0}$ has only the trivial solution.

This collects together Theorems 4.5, 4.7 and 5.4.

---

To conclude this section, we collect together some of the most important properties of matrices that we have met in this unit.

---

**Summary of properties of matrices**

Let $\mathbf{A}$ and $\mathbf{B}$ be two square matrices of the same size. Then

$$\det(\mathbf{AB}) = (\det \mathbf{A})(\det \mathbf{B}),$$

$$(\mathbf{AB})^T = \mathbf{B}^T \mathbf{A}^T,$$

$$\det \mathbf{A}^T = \det \mathbf{A}.$$

If $\mathbf{A}$ and $\mathbf{B}$ are invertible, then

$$(\mathbf{AB})^{-1} = \mathbf{B}^{-1} \mathbf{A}^{-1},$$

$$\det \mathbf{A}^{-1} = \frac{1}{\det \mathbf{A}}.$$

---

# Further exercises

**Exercise 5.10**   Let $\mathbf{A} = \begin{pmatrix} 2 & 0 \\ 4 & 1 \end{pmatrix}$ and $\mathbf{B} = \begin{pmatrix} 1 & -1 \\ -2 & 5 \end{pmatrix}$. Evaluate the following.

(a) $\det \mathbf{A}$     (b) $\det \mathbf{B}$     (c) $\det(\mathbf{A} + \mathbf{B})$

(d) $\det(\mathbf{AB})$     (e) $\det(\mathbf{BA})$     (f) $\det(\mathbf{A}^2)$

(g) $\det \mathbf{A}^T$     (h) $\det(\mathbf{AB})^T$     (i) $\det \mathbf{A}^{-1}$

**Exercise 5.11**   Determine whether or not each of the following matrices is invertible, and find the inverse where it exists.

(a) $\begin{pmatrix} 2 & 1 \\ 1 & 2 \end{pmatrix}$     (b) $\begin{pmatrix} 2 & -2 \\ -1 & 1 \end{pmatrix}$     (c) $\begin{pmatrix} 10 & 21 \\ -4 & -7 \end{pmatrix}$

**Exercise 5.12**   Evaluate the determinant of each of the following matrices.

(a) $\begin{pmatrix} 5 & -31 & 10 & 12 \\ -1 & 4 & -2 & 4 \\ 2 & 10 & 4 & 16 \\ 3 & 17 & 6 & 21 \end{pmatrix}$     (b) $\begin{pmatrix} 7 & 10 & -1 & 0 & 2 \\ 1 & 5 & 0 & 2 & 0 \\ 0 & 2 & 0 & 0 & 0 \\ 3 & -6 & 3 & 7 & 1 \\ 3 & 4 & 3 & 0 & 1 \end{pmatrix}$

**Exercise 5.13**   Determine whether or not each of the following matrices is invertible.

(a) $\begin{pmatrix} 2 & 1 & 4 \\ 1 & -1 & 3 \\ -2 & 1 & 5 \end{pmatrix}$     (b) $\begin{pmatrix} 1 & 2 & 1 \\ 2 & 1 & 2 \\ 2 & 2 & 2 \end{pmatrix}$     (c) $\begin{pmatrix} 1 & 0 & 0 & 0 \\ 2 & 1 & 0 & 0 \\ 3 & 2 & 1 & 0 \\ 4 & 3 & 2 & 1 \end{pmatrix}$

**Exercise 5.14**   Prove that an $n \times n$ matrix $\mathbf{A}$ is invertible if and only if $\mathbf{A}\mathbf{A}^T$ is invertible.

# Solutions to the exercises

**1.1 (a)** This is a linear equation.

**(b)** This is not a linear equation. The third term involves the product of $x_3$ and $x_4$.

**(c)** This is a linear equation.

**(d)** This is not a linear equation. For example, the second term, $a_2 x_2^2$, involves a product of unknowns.

**1.2** A general homogeneous system of $m$ linear equations in $n$ unknowns is

$$\begin{cases} a_{11}x_1 + \cdots + a_{1n}x_n = 0, \\ a_{21}x_1 + \cdots + a_{2n}x_n = 0, \\ \ \vdots \qquad\qquad \vdots \qquad \vdots \\ a_{m1}x_1 + \cdots + a_{mn}x_n = 0. \end{cases}$$

We substitute the values $x_1 = 0$, $x_2 = 0$, ..., $x_n = 0$ into the equations of the system:

$$\begin{cases} a_{11}0 + \cdots + a_{1n}0 = 0, \\ a_{21}0 + \cdots + a_{2n}0 = 0, \\ \ \vdots \qquad\qquad \vdots \qquad \vdots \\ a_{m1}0 + \cdots + a_{mn}0 = 0. \end{cases}$$

All the equations are satisfied, whatever the values of the coefficients $a_{ij}$. The solution set therefore contains the trivial solution

$$x_1 = 0, \ x_2 = 0, \ \ldots, \ x_n = 0.$$

**1.3** We label the equations of the system,

$$\begin{array}{ll} \mathbf{r}_1 \\ \mathbf{r}_2 \end{array} \quad \begin{cases} x + y = 4, \\ 2x - y = 5, \end{cases}$$

and apply elementary operations to simplify the system.

First we eliminate the unknown $x$ from the second equation:

$$\mathbf{r}_2 \to \mathbf{r}_2 - 2\mathbf{r}_1 \quad \begin{cases} x + y = \ \ 4, \\ \ - 3y = -3. \end{cases}$$

We then simplify this equation,

$$\mathbf{r}_2 \to -\tfrac{1}{3}\mathbf{r}_2 \quad \begin{cases} x + y = 4, \\ \quad\ y = 1, \end{cases}$$

before using it to eliminate the unknown $y$ from the first equation of the system:

$$\mathbf{r}_1 \to \mathbf{r}_1 - \mathbf{r}_2 \quad \begin{cases} x \quad\ = 3, \\ \quad\ y = 1. \end{cases}$$

We conclude that there is a unique solution—namely,

$$x = 3, \quad y = 1.$$

**1.4** We label the equations of the system,

$$\begin{array}{ll} \mathbf{r}_1 \\ \mathbf{r}_2 \\ \mathbf{r}_3 \end{array} \quad \begin{cases} x + \ y - \ z = \ \ 8, \\ 2x - \ y + \ z = \ \ 1, \\ -x + 3y + 2z = -8, \end{cases}$$

and apply elementary operations to simplify the system.

First we use the $\mathbf{r}_1$ equation to eliminate the unknown $x$ from the other equations:

$$\begin{array}{l} \mathbf{r}_2 \to \mathbf{r}_2 - 2\mathbf{r}_1 \\ \mathbf{r}_3 \to \mathbf{r}_3 + \mathbf{r}_1 \end{array} \quad \begin{cases} x + \ y - \ z = \ \ 8, \\ \quad - 3y + 3z = -15, \\ \quad \ \ 4y + \ z = \ \ 0. \end{cases}$$

We now simplify $\mathbf{r}_2$,

$$\mathbf{r}_2 \to -\tfrac{1}{3}\mathbf{r}_2 \quad \begin{cases} x + \ y - z = 8, \\ \quad\ \ y - z = 5, \\ \quad \ 4y + z = 0, \end{cases}$$

and use it to eliminate the $y$-terms from $\mathbf{r}_1$ and $\mathbf{r}_3$:

$$\begin{array}{l} \mathbf{r}_1 \to \mathbf{r}_1 - \mathbf{r}_2 \\ \\ \mathbf{r}_3 \to \mathbf{r}_3 - 4\mathbf{r}_2 \end{array} \quad \begin{cases} x \qquad\quad = \ \ 3, \\ \quad\ y - z = \ \ 5, \\ \qquad\quad 5z = -20. \end{cases}$$

We now simplify $\mathbf{r}_3$,

$$\mathbf{r}_3 \to \tfrac{1}{5}\mathbf{r}_3 \quad \begin{cases} x \qquad\quad = \ \ 3, \\ \quad\ y - z = \ \ 5, \\ \qquad\quad\ z = -4, \end{cases}$$

and use it to eliminate the $z$-term from $\mathbf{r}_2$:

$$\mathbf{r}_2 \to \mathbf{r}_2 + \mathbf{r}_3 \quad \begin{cases} x \qquad\ = \ \ 3, \\ \quad\ y \quad\ = \ \ 1, \\ \qquad\ z = -4. \end{cases}$$

We conclude that there is a unique solution—namely,

$$x = 3, \quad y = 1, \quad z = -4.$$

**1.5** We label the equations of the system, and apply elementary operations to simplify the system.

$$\begin{array}{ll} \mathbf{r}_1 \\ \mathbf{r}_2 \\ \mathbf{r}_3 \end{array} \quad \begin{cases} x + 3y - \ z = 4 \\ -x + 2y - 4z = 6 \\ x + 2y \qquad = 2 \end{cases}$$

$$\begin{array}{l} \mathbf{r}_2 \to \mathbf{r}_2 + \mathbf{r}_1 \\ \mathbf{r}_3 \to \mathbf{r}_3 - \mathbf{r}_1 \end{array} \quad \begin{cases} x + 3y - \ z = \ \ 4 \\ \quad\ \ 5y - 5z = \ 10 \\ \quad - \ y + \ z = -2 \end{cases}$$

$$\mathbf{r}_2 \to \tfrac{1}{5}\mathbf{r}_2 \quad \begin{cases} x + 3y - z = \ \ 4 \\ \quad\ \ y - z = \ \ 2 \\ \quad - y + z = -2 \end{cases}$$

$$\begin{array}{l} \mathbf{r}_1 \to \mathbf{r}_1 - 3\mathbf{r}_2 \\ \\ \mathbf{r}_3 \to \mathbf{r}_3 + \mathbf{r}_2 \end{array} \quad \begin{cases} x \qquad + 2z = -2 \\ \quad\ y - \ z = \ \ 2 \\ \qquad\quad 0 = \ \ 0 \end{cases}$$

The $\mathbf{r}_3$ equation $(0 = 0)$ gives no constraints on $x$, $y$ and $z$. We cannot simplify the system further, and conclude that there are infinitely many solutions. As both remaining equations involve a $z$-term, we set $z$ equal to the real parameter $k$, and write the general solution as

$$x = -2 - 2k, \quad y = 2 + k, \quad z = k, \quad k \in \mathbb{R}.$$

**1.6** We label the equations of the system, and apply elementary operations to simplify the system.

$$\begin{array}{l} \mathbf{r}_1 \\ \mathbf{r}_2 \\ \mathbf{r}_3 \end{array} \quad \left\{ \begin{array}{rcrcr} x + y + & z & = & 6 \\ -x + y - & 3z & = & -2 \\ 2x + y + & 3z & = & 6 \end{array} \right.$$

$$\begin{array}{l} \\ \mathbf{r}_2 \to \mathbf{r}_2 + \mathbf{r}_1 \\ \mathbf{r}_3 \to \mathbf{r}_3 - 2\mathbf{r}_1 \end{array} \quad \left\{ \begin{array}{rcrcr} x + & y + & z & = & 6 \\ & 2y - & 2z & = & 4 \\ & -y + & z & = & -6 \end{array} \right.$$

$$\begin{array}{l} \\ \mathbf{r}_2 \to \tfrac{1}{2}\mathbf{r}_2 \\ \\ \end{array} \quad \left\{ \begin{array}{rcl} x + y + z & = & 6 \\ y - z & = & 2 \\ -y + z & = & -6 \end{array} \right.$$

$$\begin{array}{l} \mathbf{r}_1 \to \mathbf{r}_1 - \mathbf{r}_2 \\ \\ \mathbf{r}_3 \to \mathbf{r}_3 + \mathbf{r}_2 \end{array} \quad \left\{ \begin{array}{rcrcr} x & + & 2z & = & 4 \\ y - & z & = & 2 \\ & 0 & = & -4 \end{array} \right.$$

The $\mathbf{r}_3$ equation is $0 = -4$, so we conclude that the solution set is empty—the system is inconsistent.

(We have chosen to use elementary operations to solve the systems of equations in the further exercises on Section 1. If you have been using the further exercises for revision, you may have preferred to use the methods of Section 2. Of course, you should obtain the same answers by either method.)

**1.7 (a)** We label the equations, and apply elementary operations to simplify the system.

$$\begin{array}{l} \mathbf{r}_1 \\ \mathbf{r}_2 \\ \mathbf{r}_3 \end{array} \quad \left\{ \begin{array}{rcr} x + 4y & = & -7 \\ 2x - y & = & 4 \\ -x + 2y & = & -5 \end{array} \right.$$

$$\begin{array}{l} \\ \mathbf{r}_2 \to \mathbf{r}_2 - 2\mathbf{r}_1 \\ \mathbf{r}_3 \to \mathbf{r}_3 + \mathbf{r}_1 \end{array} \quad \left\{ \begin{array}{rcr} x + 4y & = & -7 \\ -9y & = & 18 \\ 6y & = & -12 \end{array} \right.$$

$$\begin{array}{l} \\ \mathbf{r}_2 \to -\tfrac{1}{9}\mathbf{r}_2 \\ \\ \end{array} \quad \left\{ \begin{array}{rcr} x + 4y & = & -7 \\ y & = & -2 \\ 6y & = & -12 \end{array} \right.$$

$$\begin{array}{l} \mathbf{r}_1 \to \mathbf{r}_1 - 4\mathbf{r}_2 \\ \\ \mathbf{r}_3 \to \mathbf{r}_3 - 6\mathbf{r}_2 \end{array} \quad \left\{ \begin{array}{rcr} x & = & 1 \\ y & = & -2 \\ 0 & = & 0 \end{array} \right.$$

We conclude that there is a unique solution—namely, $x = 1$, $y = -2$.

**(b)** We label the equations, and apply elementary operations to simplify the system.

$$\begin{array}{l} \mathbf{r}_1 \\ \mathbf{r}_2 \end{array} \quad \left\{ \begin{array}{rcr} 4x - 6y & = & -2 \\ -6x + 9y & = & -3 \end{array} \right.$$

$$\begin{array}{l} \mathbf{r}_1 \to \tfrac{1}{4}\mathbf{r}_1 \\ \\ \end{array} \quad \left\{ \begin{array}{rcr} x - \tfrac{3}{2}y & = & -\tfrac{1}{2} \\ -6x + 9y & = & -3 \end{array} \right.$$

$$\begin{array}{l} \\ \mathbf{r}_2 \to \mathbf{r}_2 + 6\mathbf{r}_1 \end{array} \quad \left\{ \begin{array}{rcr} x - \tfrac{3}{2}y & = & -\tfrac{1}{2} \\ 0 & = & -6 \end{array} \right.$$

The $\mathbf{r}_2$ equation is $0 = -6$, so we conclude that the solution set is empty—the system is inconsistent.

**(c)** We label the equations, and apply elementary operations to simplify the system.

$$\begin{array}{l} \mathbf{r}_1 \\ \mathbf{r}_2 \\ \mathbf{r}_3 \end{array} \quad \left\{ \begin{array}{rcrcr} p + & q + & r & = & 5 \\ p + & 2q + & 3r & = & 11 \\ 3p + & q + & 4r & = & 13 \end{array} \right.$$

$$\begin{array}{l} \\ \mathbf{r}_2 \to \mathbf{r}_2 - \mathbf{r}_1 \\ \mathbf{r}_3 \to \mathbf{r}_3 - 3\mathbf{r}_1 \end{array} \quad \left\{ \begin{array}{rcrcr} p + & q + & r & = & 5 \\ & q + & 2r & = & 6 \\ & -2q + & r & = & -2 \end{array} \right.$$

$$\begin{array}{l} \mathbf{r}_1 \to \mathbf{r}_1 - \mathbf{r}_2 \\ \\ \mathbf{r}_3 \to \mathbf{r}_3 + 2\mathbf{r}_2 \end{array} \quad \left\{ \begin{array}{rcrcr} p & & - r & = & -1 \\ & q + & 2r & = & 6 \\ & & 5r & = & 10 \end{array} \right.$$

$$\begin{array}{l} \\ \mathbf{r}_3 \to \tfrac{1}{5}\mathbf{r}_3 \end{array} \quad \left\{ \begin{array}{rcrcr} p & & - r & = & -1 \\ & q + & 2r & = & 6 \\ & & r & = & 2 \end{array} \right.$$

$$\begin{array}{l} \mathbf{r}_1 \to \mathbf{r}_1 + \mathbf{r}_3 \\ \mathbf{r}_2 \to \mathbf{r}_2 - 2\mathbf{r}_3 \end{array} \quad \left\{ \begin{array}{rcl} p & = & 1 \\ q & = & 2 \\ r & = & 2 \end{array} \right.$$

We conclude that there is a unique solution—namely, $p = 1$, $q = 2$, $r = 2$.

**1.8** The points of intersection of the three planes correspond to the solutions of the following homogeneous system of linear equations in the three unknowns $x$, $y$ and $z$:

$$\left\{ \begin{array}{rcl} x + y - z & = & 0, \\ y - 2z & = & 0, \\ 3x - y + 5z & = & 0. \end{array} \right.$$

We label the equations, and apply elementary operations to simplify the system.

$$\begin{array}{l} \mathbf{r}_1 \\ \mathbf{r}_2 \\ \mathbf{r}_3 \end{array} \quad \left\{ \begin{array}{rcl} x + y - z & = & 0 \\ y - 2z & = & 0 \\ 3x - y + 5z & = & 0 \end{array} \right.$$

$$\begin{array}{l} \\ \\ \mathbf{r}_3 \to \mathbf{r}_3 - 3\mathbf{r}_1 \end{array} \quad \left\{ \begin{array}{rcl} x + y - z & = & 0 \\ y - 2z & = & 0 \\ -4y + 8z & = & 0 \end{array} \right.$$

$$\begin{array}{l} \mathbf{r}_1 \to \mathbf{r}_1 - \mathbf{r}_2 \\ \\ \mathbf{r}_3 \to \mathbf{r}_3 + 4\mathbf{r}_2 \end{array} \quad \left\{ \begin{array}{rcl} x + z & = & 0 \\ y - 2z & = & 0 \\ 0 & = & 0 \end{array} \right.$$

The $\mathbf{r}_3$ equation $(0 = 0)$ gives no constraints on $x$, $y$ and $z$. We cannot simplify the system further, and conclude that there are infinitely many solutions.

As both equations involve a $z$-term, we set $z$ equal to the real parameter $k$, giving

$$x = -k, \quad y = 2k, \quad z = k, \quad k \in \mathbb{R}.$$

The three planes intersect in a line.

**1.9** We label the equations, and apply elementary operations to simplify the system.

$$\begin{array}{l} \mathbf{r}_1 \\ \mathbf{r}_2 \\ \mathbf{r}_3 \\ \mathbf{r}_4 \end{array} \quad \left\{ \begin{array}{l} a - b - 2c + d = 3 \\ b + c + d = 3 \\ a - b - c + 2d = 7 \\ b + c + 2d = 7 \end{array} \right.$$

$$\begin{array}{l} \\ \\ \mathbf{r}_3 \to \mathbf{r}_3 - \mathbf{r}_1 \\ \\ \end{array} \quad \left\{ \begin{array}{l} a - b - 2c + d = 3 \\ b + c + d = 3 \\ c + d = 4 \\ b + c + 2d = 7 \end{array} \right.$$

$$\begin{array}{l} \mathbf{r}_1 \to \mathbf{r}_1 + \mathbf{r}_2 \\ \\ \\ \mathbf{r}_4 \to \mathbf{r}_4 - \mathbf{r}_2 \end{array} \quad \left\{ \begin{array}{l} a \quad - c + 2d = 6 \\ b + c + d = 3 \\ c + d = 4 \\ d = 4 \end{array} \right.$$

$$\begin{array}{l} \mathbf{r}_1 \to \mathbf{r}_1 + \mathbf{r}_3 \\ \mathbf{r}_2 \to \mathbf{r}_2 - \mathbf{r}_3 \\ \\ \end{array} \quad \left\{ \begin{array}{l} a \quad + 3d = 10 \\ b \quad = -1 \\ c + d = 4 \\ d = 4 \end{array} \right.$$

$$\begin{array}{l} \mathbf{r}_1 \to \mathbf{r}_1 - 3\mathbf{r}_4 \\ \\ \mathbf{r}_3 \to \mathbf{r}_3 - \mathbf{r}_4 \\ \\ \end{array} \quad \left\{ \begin{array}{l} a \quad = -2 \\ b \quad = -1 \\ c \quad = 0 \\ d = 4 \end{array} \right.$$

We conclude that there is a unique solution—namely, $a = -2$, $b = -1$, $c = 0$, $d = 4$.

**2.1 (a)** The augmented matrix of the system is

$$\left( \begin{array}{ccc|c} 4 & -2 & 0 & -7 \\ 0 & 1 & 3 & 0 \\ 0 & -3 & 1 & 3 \end{array} \right).$$

**(b)** The corresponding system is

$$\left\{ \begin{array}{l} 2x + 3y + 7w = 1, \\ y - 7z = -1, \\ x + 3z - w = 2. \end{array} \right.$$

**2.2 (a)** Not row-reduced; it has neither property 1 nor property 2.

**(b)** Not row-reduced; it does not have property 3.

**(c)** Row-reduced.

**(d)** Row-reduced.

**(e)** Not row-reduced; it does not have property 4.

**2.3 (a)** The augmented matrix corresponds to the system

$$\left\{ \begin{array}{l} x_1 = \frac{1}{3}, \\ x_2 = \frac{2}{3}. \end{array} \right.$$

The solution is $x_1 = \frac{1}{3}$, $x_2 = \frac{2}{3}$.

**(b)** The augmented matrix corresponds to the system

$$\left\{ \begin{array}{l} x_1 + 6x_3 = 0, \\ x_2 + 7x_3 = 0, \\ 0 = 1. \end{array} \right.$$

The third equation cannot be satisfied, so there are no solutions.

**(c)** The augmented matrix corresponds to the system

$$\left\{ \begin{array}{l} x_1 + 3x_2 + 2x_4 = -7, \\ x_3 - 3x_4 = 8, \\ x_5 = 11, \end{array} \right.$$

that is,

$$\left\{ \begin{array}{l} x_1 = -7 - 3x_2 - 2x_4, \\ x_3 = 8 + 3x_4, \\ x_5 = 11. \end{array} \right.$$

Setting $x_2 = k$ and $x_4 = l$ $(k, l \in \mathbb{R})$, we obtain the general solution

$$\begin{array}{l} x_1 = -7 - 3k - 2l, \\ x_2 = k, \\ x_3 = 8 + 3l, \\ x_4 = l, \\ x_5 = 11. \end{array}$$

**(d)** The augmented matrix corresponds to the system

$$\left\{ \begin{array}{l} x_1 + x_4 = 0, \\ x_2 + 4x_4 = 3, \\ x_3 = 0, \end{array} \right.$$

that is,

$$\left\{ \begin{array}{l} x_1 = - x_4, \\ x_2 = 3 - 4x_4, \\ x_3 = 0. \end{array} \right.$$

Setting $x_4 = k$ $(k \in \mathbb{R})$, we obtain the general solution

$$\begin{array}{l} x_1 = -k, \\ x_2 = 3 - 4k, \\ x_3 = 0, \\ x_4 = k. \end{array}$$

**2.4 (a)** We follow Strategy 2.1 in Frame 10.

If you followed Strategy 2.1, then your sequence of row operations should be the same as ours.

$$\begin{array}{l} \mathbf{r}_1 \\ \mathbf{r}_2 \\ \mathbf{r}_3 \\ \mathbf{r}_4 \end{array} \quad \left( \begin{array}{ccccc} 1 & 5 & 1 & 4 & 5 & -1 \\ 1 & 5 & 3 & 12 & 11 & 3 \\ 3 & 15 & -1 & -4 & 3 & -6 \\ -2 & -10 & 1 & 2 & -7 & 6 \end{array} \right)$$

$$\begin{array}{l} \\ \mathbf{r}_2 \to \mathbf{r}_2 - \mathbf{r}_1 \\ \mathbf{r}_3 \to \mathbf{r}_3 - 3\mathbf{r}_1 \\ \mathbf{r}_4 \to \mathbf{r}_4 + 2\mathbf{r}_1 \end{array} \quad \left( \begin{array}{ccccc} 1 & 5 & 1 & 4 & 5 & -1 \\ 0 & 0 & 2 & 8 & 6 & 4 \\ 0 & 0 & -4 & -16 & -12 & -3 \\ 0 & 0 & 3 & 10 & 3 & 4 \end{array} \right)$$

$$\begin{array}{l} \\ \mathbf{r}_2 \to \frac{1}{2}\mathbf{r}_2 \\ \\ \end{array} \quad \left( \begin{array}{ccccc} 1 & 5 & 1 & 4 & 5 & -1 \\ 0 & 0 & 1 & 4 & 3 & 2 \\ 0 & 0 & -4 & -16 & -12 & -3 \\ 0 & 0 & 3 & 10 & 3 & 4 \end{array} \right)$$

$$\begin{array}{l} \mathbf{r}_1 \to \mathbf{r}_1 - \mathbf{r}_2 \\ \\ \mathbf{r}_3 \to \mathbf{r}_3 + 4\mathbf{r}_2 \\ \mathbf{r}_4 \to \mathbf{r}_4 - 3\mathbf{r}_2 \end{array} \quad \left( \begin{array}{ccccc} 1 & 5 & 0 & 0 & 2 & -3 \\ 0 & 0 & 1 & 4 & 3 & 2 \\ 0 & 0 & 0 & 0 & 0 & 5 \\ 0 & 0 & 0 & -2 & -6 & -2 \end{array} \right)$$

$\mathbf{r}_3 \leftrightarrow \mathbf{r}_4$
$$\begin{pmatrix} 1 & 5 & 0 & 0 & 2 & -3 \\ 0 & 0 & 1 & 4 & 3 & 2 \\ 0 & 0 & 0 & -2 & -6 & -2 \\ 0 & 0 & 0 & 0 & 0 & 5 \end{pmatrix}$$

$\mathbf{r}_3 \to -\frac{1}{2}\mathbf{r}_3$
$$\begin{pmatrix} 1 & 5 & 0 & 0 & 2 & -3 \\ 0 & 0 & 1 & 4 & 3 & 2 \\ 0 & 0 & 0 & 1 & 3 & 1 \\ 0 & 0 & 0 & 0 & 0 & 5 \end{pmatrix}$$

$\mathbf{r}_2 \to \mathbf{r}_2 - 4\mathbf{r}_3$
$$\begin{pmatrix} 1 & 5 & 0 & 0 & 2 & -3 \\ 0 & 0 & 1 & 0 & -9 & -2 \\ 0 & 0 & 0 & 1 & 3 & 1 \\ 0 & 0 & 0 & 0 & 0 & 5 \end{pmatrix}$$

$\mathbf{r}_4 \to \frac{1}{5}\mathbf{r}_4$
$$\begin{pmatrix} 1 & 5 & 0 & 0 & 2 & -3 \\ 0 & 0 & 1 & 0 & -9 & -2 \\ 0 & 0 & 0 & 1 & 3 & 1 \\ 0 & 0 & 0 & 0 & 0 & 1 \end{pmatrix}$$

$\mathbf{r}_1 \to \mathbf{r}_1 + 3\mathbf{r}_4$
$\mathbf{r}_2 \to \mathbf{r}_2 + 2\mathbf{r}_4$
$\mathbf{r}_3 \to \mathbf{r}_3 - \mathbf{r}_4$
$$\begin{pmatrix} 1 & 5 & 0 & 0 & 2 & 0 \\ 0 & 0 & 1 & 0 & -9 & 0 \\ 0 & 0 & 0 & 1 & 3 & 0 \\ 0 & 0 & 0 & 0 & 0 & 1 \end{pmatrix}$$

This is the row-reduced form of the matrix.

(b) We follow Strategy 2.1 in Frame 10.

The sequence of row operations that we have used to reduce this matrix to row-reduced form might be different from the sequence that you used in following Strategy 2.1, since in the first step shown below (which corresponds to step 2 of the strategy) we chose to interchange row 1 with row 5, while you might have chosen to interchange row 1 with another row. However, your final row-reduced matrix should be the same as ours, since, by Theorem 2.1 in Frame 16, the row-reduced form of a matrix is unique.

$\mathbf{r}_1$
$\mathbf{r}_2$
$\mathbf{r}_3$
$\mathbf{r}_4$
$\mathbf{r}_5$
$$\begin{pmatrix} 0 & -8 & 8 & -14 \\ -1 & 0 & -4 & -6 \\ -1 & 8 & -12 & 8 \\ 2 & 8 & 0 & 24 \\ 1 & 4 & 0 & 14 \end{pmatrix}$$

$\mathbf{r}_1 \leftrightarrow \mathbf{r}_5$
$$\begin{pmatrix} 1 & 4 & 0 & 14 \\ -1 & 0 & -4 & -6 \\ -1 & 8 & -12 & 8 \\ 2 & 8 & 0 & 24 \\ 0 & -8 & 8 & -14 \end{pmatrix}$$

$\mathbf{r}_2 \to \mathbf{r}_2 + \mathbf{r}_1$
$\mathbf{r}_3 \to \mathbf{r}_3 + \mathbf{r}_1$
$\mathbf{r}_4 \to \mathbf{r}_4 - 2\mathbf{r}_1$
$$\begin{pmatrix} 1 & 4 & 0 & 14 \\ 0 & 4 & -4 & 8 \\ 0 & 12 & -12 & 22 \\ 0 & 0 & 0 & -4 \\ 0 & -8 & 8 & -14 \end{pmatrix}$$

$\mathbf{r}_2 \to \frac{1}{4}\mathbf{r}_2$
$$\begin{pmatrix} 1 & 4 & 0 & 14 \\ 0 & 1 & -1 & 2 \\ 0 & 12 & -12 & 22 \\ 0 & 0 & 0 & -4 \\ 0 & -8 & 8 & -14 \end{pmatrix}$$

$\mathbf{r}_1 \to \mathbf{r}_1 - 4\mathbf{r}_2$
$\mathbf{r}_3 \to \mathbf{r}_3 - 12\mathbf{r}_2$
$\mathbf{r}_5 \to \mathbf{r}_5 + 8\mathbf{r}_2$
$$\begin{pmatrix} 1 & 0 & 4 & 6 \\ 0 & 1 & -1 & 2 \\ 0 & 0 & 0 & -2 \\ 0 & 0 & 0 & -4 \\ 0 & 0 & 0 & 2 \end{pmatrix}$$

$\mathbf{r}_3 \to -\frac{1}{2}\mathbf{r}_3$
$$\begin{pmatrix} 1 & 0 & 4 & 6 \\ 0 & 1 & -1 & 2 \\ 0 & 0 & 0 & 1 \\ 0 & 0 & 0 & -4 \\ 0 & 0 & 0 & 2 \end{pmatrix}$$

$\mathbf{r}_1 \to \mathbf{r}_1 - 6\mathbf{r}_3$
$\mathbf{r}_2 \to \mathbf{r}_2 - 2\mathbf{r}_3$
$\mathbf{r}_4 \to \mathbf{r}_4 + 4\mathbf{r}_3$
$\mathbf{r}_5 \to \mathbf{r}_5 - 2\mathbf{r}_3$
$$\begin{pmatrix} 1 & 0 & 4 & 0 \\ 0 & 1 & -1 & 0 \\ 0 & 0 & 0 & 1 \\ 0 & 0 & 0 & 0 \\ 0 & 0 & 0 & 0 \end{pmatrix}$$

This is the row-reduced form of the matrix.

**2.5** In each of the following, the sequence of row operations that you used to reduce the matrix may differ from the sequence that we use, but you should obtain the same final answer.

(a) We follow Strategy 2.2 in Frame 17, and row-reduce the augmented matrix.

$\mathbf{r}_1$
$\mathbf{r}_2$
$\mathbf{r}_3$
$$\left(\begin{array}{ccc|c} 3 & 5 & -12 & 4 \\ 1 & 1 & 0 & 2 \\ 2 & 3 & -4 & 5 \end{array}\right)$$

$\mathbf{r}_1 \leftrightarrow \mathbf{r}_2$
$$\left(\begin{array}{ccc|c} 1 & 1 & 0 & 2 \\ 3 & 5 & -12 & 4 \\ 2 & 3 & -4 & 5 \end{array}\right)$$

(We have chosen to perform the row operation $\mathbf{r}_1 \leftrightarrow \mathbf{r}_2$ instead of $\mathbf{r}_1 \to \frac{1}{3}\mathbf{r}_1$, to avoid creating awkward fractions.)

$\mathbf{r}_2 \to \mathbf{r}_2 - 3\mathbf{r}_1$
$\mathbf{r}_3 \to \mathbf{r}_3 - 2\mathbf{r}_1$
$$\left(\begin{array}{ccc|c} 1 & 1 & 0 & 2 \\ 0 & 2 & -12 & -2 \\ 0 & 1 & -4 & 1 \end{array}\right)$$

$\mathbf{r}_2 \to \frac{1}{2}\mathbf{r}_2$
$$\left(\begin{array}{ccc|c} 1 & 1 & 0 & 2 \\ 0 & 1 & -6 & -1 \\ 0 & 1 & -4 & 1 \end{array}\right)$$

$\mathbf{r}_1 \to \mathbf{r}_1 - \mathbf{r}_2$
$\mathbf{r}_3 \to \mathbf{r}_3 - \mathbf{r}_2$
$$\left(\begin{array}{ccc|c} 1 & 0 & 6 & 3 \\ 0 & 1 & -6 & -1 \\ 0 & 0 & 2 & 2 \end{array}\right)$$

$\mathbf{r}_3 \to \frac{1}{2}\mathbf{r}_3$
$$\left(\begin{array}{ccc|c} 1 & 0 & 6 & 3 \\ 0 & 1 & -6 & -1 \\ 0 & 0 & 1 & 1 \end{array}\right)$$

$\mathbf{r}_1 \to \mathbf{r}_1 - 6\mathbf{r}_3$
$\mathbf{r}_2 \to \mathbf{r}_2 + 6\mathbf{r}_3$
$$\left(\begin{array}{ccc|c} 1 & 0 & 0 & -3 \\ 0 & 1 & 0 & 5 \\ 0 & 0 & 1 & 1 \end{array}\right)$$

This matrix is in row-reduced form.

The corresponding system is

$$\begin{cases} x & & = -3, \\ & y & = 5, \\ & & z = 1. \end{cases}$$

Thus the solution is $x = -3$, $y = 5$, $z = 1$.

**(b)** We follow Strategy 2.2 in Frame 17, and row-reduce the augmented matrix.

$$\begin{matrix} \mathbf{r}_1 \\ \mathbf{r}_2 \\ \mathbf{r}_3 \end{matrix} \quad \left( \begin{array}{ccccc|c} 1 & -4 & -4 & 3 & 6 & 2 \\ 2 & -5 & -6 & 6 & 9 & 3 \\ 2 & 4 & 0 & 9 & 2 & 0 \end{array} \right)$$

$$\begin{matrix} \\ \mathbf{r}_2 \to \mathbf{r}_2 - 2\mathbf{r}_1 \\ \mathbf{r}_3 \to \mathbf{r}_3 - 2\mathbf{r}_1 \end{matrix} \quad \left( \begin{array}{ccccc|c} 1 & -4 & -4 & 3 & 6 & 2 \\ 0 & 3 & 2 & 0 & -3 & -1 \\ 0 & 12 & 8 & 3 & -10 & -4 \end{array} \right)$$

$$\begin{matrix} \\ \mathbf{r}_2 \to \frac{1}{3}\mathbf{r}_2 \\ \\ \end{matrix} \quad \left( \begin{array}{ccccc|c} 1 & -4 & -4 & 3 & 6 & 2 \\ 0 & 1 & \frac{2}{3} & 0 & -1 & -\frac{1}{3} \\ 0 & 12 & 8 & 3 & -10 & -4 \end{array} \right)$$

(Note that here we cannot find a row operation that could be performed instead of $\mathbf{r}_2 \to \frac{1}{3}\mathbf{r}_2$ to create a leading 1 while avoiding fractions. Fractions are unavoidable.)

$$\begin{matrix} \mathbf{r}_1 \to \mathbf{r}_1 + 4\mathbf{r}_2 \\ \\ \mathbf{r}_3 \to \mathbf{r}_3 - 12\mathbf{r}_2 \end{matrix} \quad \left( \begin{array}{ccccc|c} 1 & 0 & -\frac{4}{3} & 3 & 2 & \frac{2}{3} \\ 0 & 1 & \frac{2}{3} & 0 & -1 & -\frac{1}{3} \\ 0 & 0 & 0 & 3 & 2 & 0 \end{array} \right)$$

$$\begin{matrix} \\ \\ \mathbf{r}_3 \to \frac{1}{3}\mathbf{r}_3 \end{matrix} \quad \left( \begin{array}{ccccc|c} 1 & 0 & -\frac{4}{3} & 3 & 2 & \frac{2}{3} \\ 0 & 1 & \frac{2}{3} & 0 & -1 & -\frac{1}{3} \\ 0 & 0 & 0 & 1 & \frac{2}{3} & 0 \end{array} \right)$$

$$\begin{matrix} \mathbf{r}_1 \to \mathbf{r}_1 - 3\mathbf{r}_3 \\ \\ \\ \end{matrix} \quad \left( \begin{array}{ccccc|c} 1 & 0 & -\frac{4}{3} & 0 & 0 & \frac{2}{3} \\ 0 & 1 & \frac{2}{3} & 0 & -1 & -\frac{1}{3} \\ 0 & 0 & 0 & 1 & \frac{2}{3} & 0 \end{array} \right)$$

This matrix is in row-reduced form.
The corresponding system is

$$\begin{cases} x_1 & -\frac{4}{3}x_3 & & = \frac{2}{3}, \\ & x_2 + \frac{2}{3}x_3 & - x_5 = -\frac{1}{3}, \\ & & x_4 + \frac{2}{3}x_5 = 0, \end{cases}$$

that is,

$$\begin{cases} x_1 = \frac{2}{3} + \frac{4}{3}x_3, \\ x_2 = -\frac{1}{3} - \frac{2}{3}x_3 + x_5, \\ x_4 = -\frac{2}{3}x_5. \end{cases}$$

Setting $x_3 = k$ and $x_5 = l$ $(k, l \in \mathbb{R})$, we obtain the general solution

$$x_1 = \frac{2}{3} + \frac{4}{3}k,$$
$$x_2 = -\frac{1}{3} - \frac{2}{3}k + l,$$
$$x_3 = k,$$
$$x_4 = -\frac{2}{3}l,$$
$$x_5 = l.$$

**2.6 (a)** Not row-reduced; it does not have property 3.

**(b)** Row-reduced.

**(c)** Row-reduced.

**(d)** Not row-reduced; it does not have property 4.

**(e)** Row-reduced.

**(f)** Row-reduced.

**2.7 (a)** The augmented matrix corresponds to the system

$$\begin{cases} x_1 & & = 7, \\ & x_2 & = -6, \\ & & x_3 = 5. \end{cases}$$

The solution is $x_1 = 7$, $x_2 = -6$, $x_3 = 5$.

**(b)** The augmented matrix corresponds to the system

$$\begin{cases} x_1 + \frac{1}{7}x_2 & = 1, \\ & x_3 = 3, \end{cases}$$

that is,

$$\begin{cases} x_1 = 1 - \frac{1}{7}x_2, \\ x_3 = 3. \end{cases}$$

Setting $x_2 = k$ $(k \in \mathbb{R})$, we obtain the general solution

$$x_1 = 1 - \frac{1}{7}k,$$
$$x_2 = k,$$
$$x_3 = 3.$$

**(c)** The augmented matrix corresponds to the system

$$\begin{cases} x_1 & + 4x_3 & = 0, \\ & x_2 - 3x_3 & = 0, \\ & & x_4 = 0, \end{cases}$$

that is,

$$\begin{cases} x_1 = -4x_3, \\ x_2 = 3x_3, \\ x_4 = 0. \end{cases}$$

Setting $x_3 = k$ $(k \in \mathbb{R})$, we obtain the general solution

$$x_1 = -4k,$$
$$x_2 = 3k,$$
$$x_3 = k,$$
$$x_4 = 0.$$

**(d)** The augmented matrix corresponds to the system

$$\begin{cases} x_1 + 3x_2 & - 2x_4 & = 0, \\ & x_3 + 2x_4 + x_5 = 0, \\ & 0 = 1. \end{cases}$$

The third equation cannot be satisfied, so there are no solutions.

**(e)** The augmented matrix corresponds to the system

$$\begin{cases} x_1 & - 5x_3 & = 4, \\ & x_2 - 7x_3 + 3x_4 = 12, \end{cases}$$

that is,

$$\begin{cases} x_1 = 4 + 5x_3, \\ x_2 = 12 + 7x_3 - 3x_4. \end{cases}$$

Setting $x_3 = k$ and $x_4 = l$ $(k, l \in \mathbb{R})$, we obtain the general solution

$$x_1 = 4 + 5k,$$
$$x_2 = 12 + 7k - 3l,$$
$$x_3 = k,$$
$$x_4 = l.$$

**2.8** We follow Strategy 2.2 in Frame 17.

**(a)** We row-reduce the augmented matrix.

$$\begin{array}{c} \mathbf{r}_1 \\ \mathbf{r}_2 \\ \mathbf{r}_3 \\ \mathbf{r}_4 \end{array} \quad \left( \begin{array}{ccc|c} 3 & -11 & -3 & 3 \\ 2 & -6 & -2 & 1 \\ 5 & -17 & -6 & 2 \\ 4 & -8 & 0 & 7 \end{array} \right)$$

$$\mathbf{r}_1 \to \mathbf{r}_1 - \mathbf{r}_2 \quad \left( \begin{array}{ccc|c} 1 & -5 & -1 & 2 \\ 2 & -6 & -2 & 1 \\ 5 & -17 & -6 & 2 \\ 4 & -8 & 0 & 7 \end{array} \right)$$

$$\begin{array}{c} \mathbf{r}_2 \to \mathbf{r}_2 - 2\mathbf{r}_1 \\ \mathbf{r}_3 \to \mathbf{r}_3 - 5\mathbf{r}_1 \\ \mathbf{r}_4 \to \mathbf{r}_4 - 4\mathbf{r}_1 \end{array} \quad \left( \begin{array}{ccc|c} 1 & -5 & -1 & 2 \\ 0 & 4 & 0 & -3 \\ 0 & 8 & -1 & -8 \\ 0 & 12 & 4 & -1 \end{array} \right)$$

$$\mathbf{r}_2 \to \tfrac{1}{4}\mathbf{r}_2 \quad \left( \begin{array}{ccc|c} 1 & -5 & -1 & 2 \\ 0 & 1 & 0 & -\tfrac{3}{4} \\ 0 & 8 & -1 & -8 \\ 0 & 12 & 4 & -1 \end{array} \right)$$

$$\begin{array}{c} \mathbf{r}_1 \to \mathbf{r}_1 + 5\mathbf{r}_2 \\ \\ \mathbf{r}_3 \to \mathbf{r}_3 - 8\mathbf{r}_2 \\ \mathbf{r}_4 \to \mathbf{r}_4 - 12\mathbf{r}_2 \end{array} \quad \left( \begin{array}{ccc|c} 1 & 0 & -1 & -\tfrac{7}{4} \\ 0 & 1 & 0 & -\tfrac{3}{4} \\ 0 & 0 & -1 & -2 \\ 0 & 0 & 4 & 8 \end{array} \right)$$

$$\mathbf{r}_3 \to -\mathbf{r}_3 \quad \left( \begin{array}{ccc|c} 1 & 0 & -1 & -\tfrac{7}{4} \\ 0 & 1 & 0 & -\tfrac{3}{4} \\ 0 & 0 & 1 & 2 \\ 0 & 0 & 4 & 8 \end{array} \right)$$

$$\mathbf{r}_1 \to \mathbf{r}_1 + \mathbf{r}_3 \quad \left( \begin{array}{ccc|c} 1 & 0 & 0 & \tfrac{1}{4} \\ 0 & 1 & 0 & -\tfrac{3}{4} \\ 0 & 0 & 1 & 2 \\ 0 & 0 & 0 & 0 \end{array} \right)$$

$$\mathbf{r}_4 \to \mathbf{r}_4 - 4\mathbf{r}_3$$

This matrix is in row-reduced form.

The corresponding system is

$$\begin{cases} x & = \tfrac{1}{4}, \\ y & = -\tfrac{3}{4}, \\ z = & 2. \end{cases}$$

Thus the solution is $x = \tfrac{1}{4}$, $y = -\tfrac{3}{4}$, $z = 2$.

**(b)** We row-reduce the augmented matrix.

$$\begin{array}{c} \mathbf{r}_1 \\ \mathbf{r}_2 \\ \mathbf{r}_3 \\ \mathbf{r}_4 \end{array} \quad \left( \begin{array}{cccc|c} 1 & 0 & -4 & -2 & -1 \\ 1 & 2 & -2 & 4 & 6 \\ 2 & 4 & -3 & 9 & 9 \\ 2 & 1 & -5 & 1 & -4 \end{array} \right)$$

$$\begin{array}{c} \mathbf{r}_2 \to \mathbf{r}_2 - \mathbf{r}_1 \\ \mathbf{r}_3 \to \mathbf{r}_3 - 2\mathbf{r}_1 \\ \mathbf{r}_4 \to \mathbf{r}_4 - 2\mathbf{r}_1 \end{array} \quad \left( \begin{array}{cccc|c} 1 & 0 & -4 & -2 & -1 \\ 0 & 2 & 2 & 6 & 7 \\ 0 & 4 & 5 & 13 & 11 \\ 0 & 1 & 3 & 5 & -2 \end{array} \right)$$

$$\mathbf{r}_2 \to \mathbf{r}_2 - \mathbf{r}_4 \quad \left( \begin{array}{cccc|c} 1 & 0 & -4 & -2 & -1 \\ 0 & 1 & -1 & 1 & 9 \\ 0 & 4 & 5 & 13 & 11 \\ 0 & 1 & 3 & 5 & -2 \end{array} \right)$$

$$\begin{array}{c} \mathbf{r}_3 \to \mathbf{r}_3 - 4\mathbf{r}_2 \\ \mathbf{r}_4 \to \mathbf{r}_4 - \mathbf{r}_2 \end{array} \quad \left( \begin{array}{cccc|c} 1 & 0 & -4 & -2 & -1 \\ 0 & 1 & -1 & 1 & 9 \\ 0 & 0 & 9 & 9 & -25 \\ 0 & 0 & 4 & 4 & -11 \end{array} \right)$$

$$\mathbf{r}_3 \to \mathbf{r}_3 - 2\mathbf{r}_4 \quad \left( \begin{array}{cccc|c} 1 & 0 & -4 & -2 & -1 \\ 0 & 1 & -1 & 1 & 9 \\ 0 & 0 & 1 & 1 & -3 \\ 0 & 0 & 4 & 4 & -11 \end{array} \right)$$

$$\begin{array}{c} \mathbf{r}_1 \to \mathbf{r}_1 + 4\mathbf{r}_3 \\ \mathbf{r}_2 \to \mathbf{r}_2 + \mathbf{r}_3 \\ \\ \mathbf{r}_4 \to \mathbf{r}_4 - 4\mathbf{r}_3 \end{array} \quad \left( \begin{array}{cccc|c} 1 & 0 & 0 & 2 & -13 \\ 0 & 1 & 0 & 2 & 6 \\ 0 & 0 & 1 & 1 & -3 \\ 0 & 0 & 0 & 0 & 1 \end{array} \right)$$

This matrix is in row-reduced form.
The corresponding system is

$$\begin{cases} a & + 2d = -13, \\ b & + 2d = 6, \\ c + d = -3, \\ 0 = 1. \end{cases}$$

The fourth equation cannot be satisfied, so there are no solutions.

The last matrix in the above row-reduction corresponds to a system containing the equation $0 = 1$. We could have concluded that the given system has no solutions at this point.

(c) We row-reduce the augmented matrix.

$$\begin{array}{c}\mathbf{r}_1\\\mathbf{r}_2\\\mathbf{r}_3\\\mathbf{r}_4\end{array}\left(\begin{array}{ccccc|c}2 & 2 & -5 & 6 & 10 & -2\\2 & 2 & -6 & 6 & 8 & 0\\2 & 0 & -1 & 2 & 7 & 7\\1 & 2 & -5 & 5 & 4 & -3\end{array}\right)$$

$$\begin{array}{c}\mathbf{r}_1\leftrightarrow\mathbf{r}_4\end{array}\left(\begin{array}{ccccc|c}1 & 2 & -5 & 5 & 4 & -3\\2 & 2 & -6 & 6 & 8 & 0\\2 & 0 & -1 & 2 & 7 & 7\\2 & 2 & -5 & 6 & 10 & -2\end{array}\right)$$

$$\begin{array}{c}\\\mathbf{r}_2\to\mathbf{r}_2-2\mathbf{r}_1\\\mathbf{r}_3\to\mathbf{r}_3-2\mathbf{r}_1\\\mathbf{r}_4\to\mathbf{r}_4-2\mathbf{r}_1\end{array}\left(\begin{array}{ccccc|c}1 & 2 & -5 & 5 & 4 & -3\\0 & -2 & 4 & -4 & 0 & 6\\0 & -4 & 9 & -8 & -1 & 13\\0 & -2 & 5 & -4 & 2 & 4\end{array}\right)$$

$$\begin{array}{c}\\\mathbf{r}_2\to-\tfrac{1}{2}\mathbf{r}_2\\\\\end{array}\left(\begin{array}{ccccc|c}1 & 2 & -5 & 5 & 4 & -3\\0 & 1 & -2 & 2 & 0 & -3\\0 & -4 & 9 & -8 & -1 & 13\\0 & -2 & 5 & -4 & 2 & 4\end{array}\right)$$

$$\begin{array}{c}\mathbf{r}_1\to\mathbf{r}_1-2\mathbf{r}_2\\\\\mathbf{r}_3\to\mathbf{r}_3+4\mathbf{r}_2\\\mathbf{r}_4\to\mathbf{r}_4+2\mathbf{r}_2\end{array}\left(\begin{array}{ccccc|c}1 & 0 & -1 & 1 & 4 & 3\\0 & 1 & -2 & 2 & 0 & -3\\0 & 0 & 1 & 0 & -1 & 1\\0 & 0 & 1 & 0 & 2 & -2\end{array}\right)$$

$$\begin{array}{c}\mathbf{r}_1\to\mathbf{r}_1+\mathbf{r}_3\\\mathbf{r}_2\to\mathbf{r}_2+2\mathbf{r}_3\\\\\mathbf{r}_4\to\mathbf{r}_4-\mathbf{r}_3\end{array}\left(\begin{array}{ccccc|c}1 & 0 & 0 & 1 & 3 & 4\\0 & 1 & 0 & 2 & -2 & -1\\0 & 0 & 1 & 0 & -1 & 1\\0 & 0 & 0 & 0 & 3 & -3\end{array}\right)$$

$$\begin{array}{c}\\\\\\\mathbf{r}_4\to\tfrac{1}{3}\mathbf{r}_4\end{array}\left(\begin{array}{ccccc|c}1 & 0 & 0 & 1 & 3 & 4\\0 & 1 & 0 & 2 & -2 & -1\\0 & 0 & 1 & 0 & -1 & 1\\0 & 0 & 0 & 0 & 1 & -1\end{array}\right)$$

$$\begin{array}{c}\mathbf{r}_1\to\mathbf{r}_1-3\mathbf{r}_4\\\mathbf{r}_2\to\mathbf{r}_2+2\mathbf{r}_4\\\mathbf{r}_3\to\mathbf{r}_3+\mathbf{r}_4\\\\\end{array}\left(\begin{array}{ccccc|c}1 & 0 & 0 & 1 & 0 & 7\\0 & 1 & 0 & 2 & 0 & -3\\0 & 0 & 1 & 0 & 0 & 0\\0 & 0 & 0 & 0 & 1 & -1\end{array}\right)$$

This matrix is in row-reduced form.
The corresponding system is

$$\begin{cases}x_1 & & & +\ x_4 & & =\ 7,\\ & x_2 & & +\ 2x_4 & & =\ -3,\\ & & x_3 & & & =\ 0,\\ & & & & x_5 & =\ -1,\end{cases}$$

that is,

$$\begin{cases}x_1 =\ 7-\ x_4,\\ x_2 = -3-2x_4,\\ x_3 =\ 0,\\ x_5 = -1.\end{cases}$$

Setting $x_4 = k$ $(k \in \mathbb{R})$, we obtain the general solution

$$\begin{aligned}x_1 &= 7-k,\\x_2 &= -3-2k,\\x_3 &= 0,\\x_4 &= k,\\x_5 &= -1.\end{aligned}$$

**3.1** (a) This is a $2 \times 4$ matrix, so it is not square. The $(2,3)$-entry is 5.

(b) This is a $3 \times 3$ matrix, so it is square. The $(2,3)$-entry is 0.

(c) This is a $2 \times 2$ matrix, so it is square. There is no $(2,3)$-entry.

**3.2** We add corresponding entries.

(a) $\begin{pmatrix}1 & -3\\-2 & 54\end{pmatrix} + \begin{pmatrix}2 & 0\\4 & 1\end{pmatrix} = \begin{pmatrix}3 & -3\\2 & 55\end{pmatrix}$

(b) $\begin{pmatrix}2 & 0\\4 & 1\end{pmatrix} + \begin{pmatrix}1 & -3\\-2 & 54\end{pmatrix} = \begin{pmatrix}3 & -3\\2 & 55\end{pmatrix}$

(c) This sum cannot be evaluated, since the matrices are of different sizes.

(d) $\begin{pmatrix}0 & 6 & -2\\1 & 8 & 2\\0 & 3 & 4\end{pmatrix} + \begin{pmatrix}1 & 2 & 9\\1 & 0 & 4\\3 & -4 & 1\end{pmatrix}$

$= \begin{pmatrix}1 & 8 & 7\\2 & 8 & 6\\3 & -1 & 5\end{pmatrix}$

**3.3** We add corresponding entries of the three matrices $\mathbf{A} = (a_{ij})$, $\mathbf{B} = (b_{ij})$ and $\mathbf{C} = (c_{ij})$. The $(i,j)$-entry of the matrix $\mathbf{A} + (\mathbf{B} + \mathbf{C})$ is $a_{ij} + (b_{ij} + c_{ij})$, and that of $(\mathbf{A} + \mathbf{B}) + \mathbf{C}$ is $(a_{ij} + b_{ij}) + c_{ij}$. Now, $a_{ij}$, $b_{ij}$ and $c_{ij}$ are scalars, and scalar addition is associative, so $a_{ij} + (b_{ij} + c_{ij}) = (a_{ij} + b_{ij}) + c_{ij}$. Therefore
$$\mathbf{A} + (\mathbf{B} + \mathbf{C}) = (\mathbf{A} + \mathbf{B}) + \mathbf{C}.$$

**3.4** We add corresponding entries of the two matrices. The $(i,j)$-entry of the matrix $\mathbf{A} + \mathbf{0}$ is $a_{ij} + 0 = a_{ij}$. Therefore
$$\mathbf{A} + \mathbf{0} = \mathbf{A}.$$

**3.5** (a) This difference cannot be evaluated, since the matrices are of different sizes.

(b) $\begin{pmatrix}5 & 8 & 12\\7 & 2 & -1\end{pmatrix} - \begin{pmatrix}3 & 10 & 2\\4 & 9 & 21\end{pmatrix}$

$= \begin{pmatrix}2 & -2 & 10\\3 & -7 & -22\end{pmatrix}$

**3.6** (a) $4\mathbf{A} = 4\begin{pmatrix}5 & -3\\2 & 3\\-1 & 0\end{pmatrix} = \begin{pmatrix}20 & -12\\8 & 12\\-4 & 0\end{pmatrix}$

(b) $4\mathbf{B} = 4\begin{pmatrix}2 & 1\\-2 & -7\\3 & 5\end{pmatrix} = \begin{pmatrix}8 & 4\\-8 & -28\\12 & 20\end{pmatrix}$

(c) $4\mathbf{A} + 4\mathbf{B} = \begin{pmatrix}20 & -12\\8 & 12\\-4 & 0\end{pmatrix} + \begin{pmatrix}8 & 4\\-8 & -28\\12 & 20\end{pmatrix}$

$= \begin{pmatrix}28 & -8\\0 & -16\\8 & 20\end{pmatrix}$

(d) $\mathbf{A} + \mathbf{B} = \begin{pmatrix} 5 & -3 \\ 2 & 3 \\ -1 & 0 \end{pmatrix} + \begin{pmatrix} 2 & 1 \\ -2 & -7 \\ 3 & 5 \end{pmatrix}$

$= \begin{pmatrix} 7 & -2 \\ 0 & -4 \\ 2 & 5 \end{pmatrix}$,

thus

$4(\mathbf{A} + \mathbf{B}) = \begin{pmatrix} 28 & -8 \\ 0 & -16 \\ 8 & 20 \end{pmatrix}$.

**3.7** To obtain the $(2, 1)$-entry of the product $\mathbf{AB}$, we take the dot product of the second row of $\mathbf{A}$ with the first column of $\mathbf{B}$. The $(2, 1)$-entry of $\mathbf{AB}$ is

$(4, 5, 6) \cdot (1, 4, 7) = (4 \times 1) + (5 \times 4) + (6 \times 7)$
$= 4 + 20 + 42$
$= 66.$

**3.8 (a)** The product of a $3 \times 2$ matrix with a $2 \times 1$ matrix is a $3 \times 1$ matrix:

$\begin{pmatrix} 2 & -1 \\ 0 & 3 \\ 1 & 2 \end{pmatrix} \begin{pmatrix} 3 \\ 2 \end{pmatrix} = \begin{pmatrix} 4 \\ 6 \\ 7 \end{pmatrix}$.

**(b)** The product of a $1 \times 2$ matrix with a $2 \times 2$ matrix is a $1 \times 2$ matrix:

$(2 \quad 1) \begin{pmatrix} 1 & 6 \\ 0 & 2 \end{pmatrix} = (2 \quad 14)$.

**(c)** This product cannot be formed, since the first matrix has 1 column and the second has 2 rows.

**(d)** The product of a $2 \times 1$ matrix with a $1 \times 3$ matrix is a $2 \times 3$ matrix:

$\begin{pmatrix} 1 \\ 2 \end{pmatrix} (3 \quad 0 \quad -4) = \begin{pmatrix} 3 & 0 & -4 \\ 6 & 0 & -8 \end{pmatrix}$.

**(e)** The product of a $2 \times 3$ matrix with a $3 \times 3$ matrix is a $2 \times 3$ matrix:

$\begin{pmatrix} 3 & 1 & 2 \\ 0 & 5 & 1 \end{pmatrix} \begin{pmatrix} -2 & 0 & 1 \\ 1 & 3 & 0 \\ 4 & 1 & -1 \end{pmatrix}$

$= \begin{pmatrix} 3 & 5 & 1 \\ 9 & 16 & -1 \end{pmatrix}$.

**3.9** The product of a $2 \times 2$ matrix with a $2 \times 2$ matrix is a $2 \times 2$ matrix. The products $\mathbf{AB}$ and $\mathbf{BA}$ are therefore both $2 \times 2$ matrices:

$\mathbf{AB} = \begin{pmatrix} 1 & 1 \\ 3 & 2 \end{pmatrix} \begin{pmatrix} 1 & 4 \\ 2 & 1 \end{pmatrix} = \begin{pmatrix} 3 & 5 \\ 7 & 14 \end{pmatrix}$,

$\mathbf{BA} = \begin{pmatrix} 1 & 4 \\ 2 & 1 \end{pmatrix} \begin{pmatrix} 1 & 1 \\ 3 & 2 \end{pmatrix} = \begin{pmatrix} 13 & 9 \\ 5 & 4 \end{pmatrix}$.

The products $\mathbf{AB}$ and $\mathbf{BA}$ are not the same.

Matrix multiplication is therefore not commutative.

**3.10** The product of a $2 \times 2$ matrix with a $2 \times 2$ matrix is a $2 \times 2$ matrix.

**(a)** $\mathbf{AB} = \begin{pmatrix} 1 & 0 \\ 0 & 7 \end{pmatrix} \begin{pmatrix} -3 & 0 \\ 0 & 4 \end{pmatrix} = \begin{pmatrix} -3 & 0 \\ 0 & 28 \end{pmatrix}$.

**(b)** $\mathbf{BA} = \begin{pmatrix} -3 & 0 \\ 0 & 4 \end{pmatrix} \begin{pmatrix} 1 & 0 \\ 0 & 7 \end{pmatrix} = \begin{pmatrix} -3 & 0 \\ 0 & 28 \end{pmatrix}$.

Note that $\mathbf{AB}$ and $\mathbf{BA}$ are equal in this case.

**(c)** Matrix multiplication is associative, so

$\mathbf{ABC} = (\mathbf{AB})\mathbf{C} = \mathbf{A}(\mathbf{BC})$

$= \left( \begin{pmatrix} 1 & 0 \\ 0 & 7 \end{pmatrix} \begin{pmatrix} -3 & 0 \\ 0 & 4 \end{pmatrix} \right) \begin{pmatrix} 2 & 0 \\ 0 & 12 \end{pmatrix}$

$= \begin{pmatrix} -3 & 0 \\ 0 & 28 \end{pmatrix} \begin{pmatrix} 2 & 0 \\ 0 & 12 \end{pmatrix}$

$= \begin{pmatrix} -6 & 0 \\ 0 & 336 \end{pmatrix}$.

**3.11 (a)** The matrix $\begin{pmatrix} 1 & 1 & 1 \\ 0 & 2 & 2 \\ 0 & 0 & 3 \end{pmatrix}$ is upper-triangular.

**(b)** The matrix $\begin{pmatrix} 9 & 0 \\ 0 & 0 \end{pmatrix}$ is diagonal, upper-triangular and lower-triangular.

**(c)** The matrix $\begin{pmatrix} 0 & 0 & 1 \\ 0 & 1 & 2 \\ 1 & 2 & 3 \end{pmatrix}$ is *not* diagonal, upper-triangular or lower-triangular.

**(d)** The matrix $\begin{pmatrix} 1 & 0 \\ 1 & 0 \end{pmatrix}$ is lower-triangular.

**3.12 (a)** The transpose of a $3 \times 2$ matrix is a $2 \times 3$ matrix:

$\begin{pmatrix} 1 & 4 \\ 0 & 2 \\ -6 & 10 \end{pmatrix}^T = \begin{pmatrix} 1 & 0 & -6 \\ 4 & 2 & 10 \end{pmatrix}$.

**(b)** The transpose of a $3 \times 3$ matrix is a $3 \times 3$ matrix:

$\begin{pmatrix} 2 & 1 & 2 \\ 0 & 3 & -5 \\ 4 & 7 & 0 \end{pmatrix}^T = \begin{pmatrix} 2 & 0 & 4 \\ 1 & 3 & 7 \\ 2 & -5 & 0 \end{pmatrix}$.

**(c)** The transpose of a $1 \times 3$ matrix is a $3 \times 1$ matrix:

$(10 \quad 4 \quad 6)^T = \begin{pmatrix} 10 \\ 4 \\ 6 \end{pmatrix}$.

**(d)** The transpose of a $2 \times 2$ matrix is a $2 \times 2$ matrix:

$\begin{pmatrix} 1 & 0 \\ 0 & 2 \end{pmatrix}^T = \begin{pmatrix} 1 & 0 \\ 0 & 2 \end{pmatrix}$.

In fact, $\mathbf{A}^T = \mathbf{A}$ for all *diagonal* matrices.

**3.13 (a)** Here,

$\mathbf{A}^T = \begin{pmatrix} 1 & 3 & 5 \\ 2 & 4 & 6 \end{pmatrix}$,

$\mathbf{B}^T = \begin{pmatrix} 7 & 9 & 11 \\ 8 & 10 & 12 \end{pmatrix}$

and
$$\mathbf{A} + \mathbf{B} = \begin{pmatrix} 8 & 10 \\ 12 & 14 \\ 16 & 18 \end{pmatrix}.$$

So
$$(\mathbf{A} + \mathbf{B})^T = \begin{pmatrix} 8 & 12 & 16 \\ 10 & 14 & 18 \end{pmatrix}$$

and
$$\mathbf{A}^T + \mathbf{B}^T = \begin{pmatrix} 1 & 3 & 5 \\ 2 & 4 & 6 \end{pmatrix} + \begin{pmatrix} 7 & 9 & 11 \\ 8 & 10 & 12 \end{pmatrix}$$
$$= \begin{pmatrix} 8 & 12 & 16 \\ 10 & 14 & 18 \end{pmatrix}$$
$$= (\mathbf{A} + \mathbf{B})^T.$$

(b) Here,
$$\mathbf{C}^T = \begin{pmatrix} 1 & 1 \\ 0 & 1 \end{pmatrix}$$

and
$$\mathbf{A}\mathbf{C} = \begin{pmatrix} 1 & 2 \\ 3 & 4 \\ 5 & 6 \end{pmatrix} \begin{pmatrix} 1 & 0 \\ 1 & 1 \end{pmatrix} = \begin{pmatrix} 3 & 2 \\ 7 & 4 \\ 11 & 6 \end{pmatrix}.$$

So
$$(\mathbf{A}\mathbf{C})^T = \begin{pmatrix} 3 & 7 & 11 \\ 2 & 4 & 6 \end{pmatrix}.$$

The product $\mathbf{A}^T \mathbf{C}^T$ cannot be formed, since $\mathbf{A}^T$ is a $2 \times 3$ matrix and $\mathbf{C}^T$ is a $2 \times 2$ matrix.
The product $\mathbf{C}^T \mathbf{A}^T$ does, however, exist:
$$\mathbf{C}^T \mathbf{A}^T = \begin{pmatrix} 1 & 1 \\ 0 & 1 \end{pmatrix} \begin{pmatrix} 1 & 3 & 5 \\ 2 & 4 & 6 \end{pmatrix}$$
$$= \begin{pmatrix} 3 & 7 & 11 \\ 2 & 4 & 6 \end{pmatrix}$$
$$= (\mathbf{A}\mathbf{C})^T.$$

**3.14** (a) $\mathbf{A} + \mathbf{B} = \begin{pmatrix} 3 & 3 \\ 3 & 3 \end{pmatrix}$

(b) $\mathbf{A} - \mathbf{B} = \begin{pmatrix} -1 & 9 \\ 3 & -11 \end{pmatrix}$

(c) $\mathbf{B} - \mathbf{A} = -(\mathbf{A} - \mathbf{B}) = \begin{pmatrix} 1 & -9 \\ -3 & 11 \end{pmatrix}$

(d) $\mathbf{A}\mathbf{B} = \begin{pmatrix} 2 & 39 \\ 6 & -37 \end{pmatrix}$

(e) $\mathbf{B}\mathbf{A} = \begin{pmatrix} -7 & 24 \\ 21 & -28 \end{pmatrix}$

(f) $\mathbf{A}^2 = \begin{pmatrix} 19 & -18 \\ -9 & 34 \end{pmatrix}$

(g) $\mathbf{A}^T = \begin{pmatrix} 1 & 3 \\ 6 & -4 \end{pmatrix}$

(h) $\mathbf{B}^T = \begin{pmatrix} 2 & 0 \\ -3 & 7 \end{pmatrix}$

(i) $\mathbf{A}^T \mathbf{B}^T = (\mathbf{B}\mathbf{A})^T = \begin{pmatrix} -7 & 21 \\ 24 & -28 \end{pmatrix}$

**3.15** (a) $\mathbf{F}\mathbf{B} : 3 \times 3$, $\mathbf{E} : 3 \times 3$.
The matrix $\mathbf{F}\mathbf{B} + \mathbf{E}$ exists and is $3 \times 3$.

(b) $\mathbf{F}^T : 4 \times 3$, $\mathbf{G}\mathbf{F}^T : 2 \times 3$, $\mathbf{A}\mathbf{D} : 2 \times 4$, $\mathbf{A}\mathbf{D}\mathbf{B} : 2 \times 3$.
The matrix $\mathbf{G}\mathbf{F}^T - \mathbf{A}\mathbf{D}\mathbf{B}$ exists and is $2 \times 3$.

(c) $\mathbf{B}\mathbf{F} : 4 \times 4$, $\mathbf{F}\mathbf{B} : 3 \times 3$, $(\mathbf{F}\mathbf{B})^T : 3 \times 3$.
The matrix $\mathbf{B}\mathbf{F} - (\mathbf{F}\mathbf{B})^T$ does not exist, since $\mathbf{B}\mathbf{F}$ and $(\mathbf{F}\mathbf{B})^T$ are different sizes.

(d) $\mathbf{A}\mathbf{D} : 2 \times 4$, $\mathbf{A}\mathbf{D} + \mathbf{G} : 2 \times 4$, $\mathbf{C} : 3 \times 2$.
The matrix $\mathbf{C}(\mathbf{A}\mathbf{D} + \mathbf{G})$ exists and is $3 \times 4$.

(e) $\mathbf{C}\mathbf{A} : 3 \times 1$, $(\mathbf{C}\mathbf{A})^T : 1 \times 3$, $\mathbf{D} : 1 \times 4$.
The matrix $(\mathbf{C}\mathbf{A})^T \mathbf{D}$ does not exist, since $(\mathbf{C}\mathbf{A})^T$ is size $1 \times 3$ and $\mathbf{D}$ is size $1 \times 4$.

(f) $\mathbf{E}^T \mathbf{B}^T \mathbf{G}^T \mathbf{C}^T = (\mathbf{C}\mathbf{G}\mathbf{B}\mathbf{E})^T$.
$\mathbf{C}\mathbf{G} : 3 \times 4$, $\mathbf{C}\mathbf{G}\mathbf{B} : 3 \times 3$, $\mathbf{C}\mathbf{G}\mathbf{B}\mathbf{E} : 3 \times 3$, $(\mathbf{C}\mathbf{G}\mathbf{B}\mathbf{E})^T : 3 \times 3$.
The matrix $\mathbf{E}^T \mathbf{B}^T \mathbf{G}^T \mathbf{C}^T$ exists and is $3 \times 3$.

**3.16** Let $\mathbf{A} = (a_{ij})$ and $\mathbf{B} = (b_{ij})$ be matrices of the same size. Then the $(i, j)$-entry of $k(\mathbf{A} + \mathbf{B})$ is $k(a_{ij} + b_{ij})$.
Now, $k\mathbf{A} = (ka_{ij})$ and $k\mathbf{B} = (kb_{ij})$, so the $(i, j)$-entry of $k\mathbf{A} + k\mathbf{B}$ is $ka_{ij} + kb_{ij} = k(a_{ij} + b_{ij})$.
The $(i, j)$-entries of $k(\mathbf{A} + \mathbf{B})$ and $k\mathbf{A} + k\mathbf{B}$ are equal. Thus
$$k(\mathbf{A} + \mathbf{B}) = k\mathbf{A} + k\mathbf{B}.$$

**3.17** The $(i, j)$-entry of the product $\mathbf{I}_m \mathbf{A}$ is obtained by taking the dot product of the $i$th row of $\mathbf{I}_m$ with the $j$th column of $\mathbf{A}$. Now, the $i$th row of $\mathbf{I}_m$ has a 1 in the $i$th position and 0s elsewhere. Therefore the dot product will give the $i$th entry of the $j$th column of $\mathbf{A}$, that is, the $(i, j)$-entry of $\mathbf{A}$. Thus $\mathbf{I}_m \mathbf{A} = \mathbf{A}$.
The $(i, j)$-entry of the product $\mathbf{A}\mathbf{I}_n$ is obtained by taking the dot product of the $i$th row of $\mathbf{A}$ with the $j$th column of $\mathbf{I}_n$. Now, the $j$th column of $\mathbf{I}_n$ has a 1 in the $j$th position and 0s elsewhere. Therefore the dot product will give the $j$th entry of the $i$th row of $\mathbf{A}$, that is, the $(i, j)$-entry of $\mathbf{A}$. Thus $\mathbf{A}\mathbf{I}_n = \mathbf{A}$.

**4.1** Suppose, for a contradiction, that there exists a matrix $\mathbf{B} = \begin{pmatrix} a & b \\ c & d \end{pmatrix}$ such that $\mathbf{A}\mathbf{B} = \mathbf{I}$, that is,
$$\begin{pmatrix} 1 & -1 \\ -1 & 1 \end{pmatrix} \begin{pmatrix} a & b \\ c & d \end{pmatrix} = \begin{pmatrix} 1 & 0 \\ 0 & 1 \end{pmatrix}.$$
Multiplying out the matrices on the left-hand side:
$$\begin{pmatrix} a - c & b - d \\ -a + c & -b + d \end{pmatrix} = \begin{pmatrix} 1 & 0 \\ 0 & 1 \end{pmatrix}.$$
Looking at the entries in the first column, we must have $a - c = 1$ and $-a + c = 0$, that is, $a - c = 1$ and $a - c = 0$. This contradiction shows that there exists no such matrix $\mathbf{B}$. (A similar conclusion arises from looking at the entries in the second column.)

**4.2** The equation $\mathbf{II} = \mathbf{I}$ shows that $\mathbf{I}$ is invertible, with inverse $\mathbf{I}$.

**4.3** To prove that $\mathbf{AB}$ is invertible, with inverse $\mathbf{B}^{-1}\mathbf{A}^{-1}$, we have to show that

$$(\mathbf{AB})(\mathbf{B}^{-1}\mathbf{A}^{-1}) = \mathbf{I} \quad \text{and} \quad (\mathbf{B}^{-1}\mathbf{A}^{-1})(\mathbf{AB}) = \mathbf{I}.$$

But, by associativity,

$$(\mathbf{AB})(\mathbf{B}^{-1}\mathbf{A}^{-1}) = \mathbf{A}(\mathbf{BB}^{-1})\mathbf{A}^{-1}$$
$$= \mathbf{AIA}^{-1}$$
$$= \mathbf{AA}^{-1} = \mathbf{I},$$

and, similarly,

$$(\mathbf{B}^{-1}\mathbf{A}^{-1})(\mathbf{AB}) = \mathbf{B}^{-1}(\mathbf{A}^{-1}\mathbf{A})\mathbf{B}$$
$$= \mathbf{B}^{-1}\mathbf{IB}$$
$$= \mathbf{B}^{-1}\mathbf{B} = \mathbf{I}.$$

The required result follows.

**4.4 (a)** We row-reduce $(\mathbf{A} \mid \mathbf{I})$.

$$\begin{array}{c} \mathbf{r}_1 \\ \mathbf{r}_2 \end{array} \quad \left( \begin{array}{cc|cc} 2 & 4 & 1 & 0 \\ 4 & 1 & 0 & 1 \end{array} \right)$$

$$\mathbf{r}_1 \to \tfrac{1}{2}\mathbf{r}_1 \quad \left( \begin{array}{cc|cc} 1 & 2 & \tfrac{1}{2} & 0 \\ 4 & 1 & 0 & 1 \end{array} \right)$$

$$\mathbf{r}_2 \to \mathbf{r}_2 - 4\mathbf{r}_1 \quad \left( \begin{array}{cc|cc} 1 & 2 & \tfrac{1}{2} & 0 \\ 0 & -7 & -2 & 1 \end{array} \right)$$

$$\mathbf{r}_2 \to -\tfrac{1}{7}\mathbf{r}_2 \quad \left( \begin{array}{cc|cc} 1 & 2 & \tfrac{1}{2} & 0 \\ 0 & 1 & \tfrac{2}{7} & -\tfrac{1}{7} \end{array} \right)$$

$$\mathbf{r}_1 \to \mathbf{r}_1 - 2\mathbf{r}_2 \quad \left( \begin{array}{cc|cc} 1 & 0 & -\tfrac{1}{14} & \tfrac{2}{7} \\ 0 & 1 & \tfrac{2}{7} & -\tfrac{1}{7} \end{array} \right)$$

The left half has been reduced to $\mathbf{I}$, so the given matrix is invertible; its inverse is

$$\left( \begin{array}{cc} -\tfrac{1}{14} & \tfrac{2}{7} \\ \tfrac{2}{7} & -\tfrac{1}{7} \end{array} \right).$$

**(b)** We row-reduce $(\mathbf{A} \mid \mathbf{I})$.

$$\begin{array}{c} \mathbf{r}_1 \\ \mathbf{r}_2 \\ \mathbf{r}_3 \end{array} \quad \left( \begin{array}{ccc|ccc} 1 & 1 & -4 & 1 & 0 & 0 \\ 2 & 1 & -6 & 0 & 1 & 0 \\ -3 & -1 & 9 & 0 & 0 & 1 \end{array} \right)$$

$$\begin{array}{c} \mathbf{r}_2 \to \mathbf{r}_2 - 2\mathbf{r}_1 \\ \mathbf{r}_3 \to \mathbf{r}_3 + 3\mathbf{r}_1 \end{array} \quad \left( \begin{array}{ccc|ccc} 1 & 1 & -4 & 1 & 0 & 0 \\ 0 & -1 & 2 & -2 & 1 & 0 \\ 0 & 2 & -3 & 3 & 0 & 1 \end{array} \right)$$

$$\mathbf{r}_2 \to -\mathbf{r}_2 \quad \left( \begin{array}{ccc|ccc} 1 & 1 & -4 & 1 & 0 & 0 \\ 0 & 1 & -2 & 2 & -1 & 0 \\ 0 & 2 & -3 & 3 & 0 & 1 \end{array} \right)$$

$$\begin{array}{c} \mathbf{r}_1 \to \mathbf{r}_1 - \mathbf{r}_2 \\ \\ \mathbf{r}_3 \to \mathbf{r}_3 - 2\mathbf{r}_2 \end{array} \quad \left( \begin{array}{ccc|ccc} 1 & 0 & -2 & -1 & 1 & 0 \\ 0 & 1 & -2 & 2 & -1 & 0 \\ 0 & 0 & 1 & -1 & 2 & 1 \end{array} \right)$$

$$\begin{array}{c} \mathbf{r}_1 \to \mathbf{r}_1 + 2\mathbf{r}_3 \\ \mathbf{r}_2 \to \mathbf{r}_2 + 2\mathbf{r}_3 \end{array} \quad \left( \begin{array}{ccc|ccc} 1 & 0 & 0 & -3 & 5 & 2 \\ 0 & 1 & 0 & 0 & 3 & 2 \\ 0 & 0 & 1 & -1 & 2 & 1 \end{array} \right)$$

The left half has been reduced to $\mathbf{I}$, so the given matrix is invertible; its inverse is

$$\left( \begin{array}{ccc} -3 & 5 & 2 \\ 0 & 3 & 2 \\ -1 & 2 & 1 \end{array} \right).$$

**(c)** We row-reduce $(\mathbf{A} \mid \mathbf{I})$.

$$\begin{array}{c} \mathbf{r}_1 \\ \mathbf{r}_2 \\ \mathbf{r}_3 \end{array} \quad \left( \begin{array}{ccc|ccc} 2 & 4 & 6 & 1 & 0 & 0 \\ 1 & 2 & 4 & 0 & 1 & 0 \\ 5 & 10 & 5 & 0 & 0 & 1 \end{array} \right)$$

$$\mathbf{r}_1 \to \tfrac{1}{2}\mathbf{r}_1 \quad \left( \begin{array}{ccc|ccc} 1 & 2 & 3 & \tfrac{1}{2} & 0 & 0 \\ 1 & 2 & 4 & 0 & 1 & 0 \\ 5 & 10 & 5 & 0 & 0 & 1 \end{array} \right)$$

$$\begin{array}{c} \mathbf{r}_2 \to \mathbf{r}_2 - \mathbf{r}_1 \\ \\ \mathbf{r}_3 \to \mathbf{r}_3 - 5\mathbf{r}_1 \end{array} \quad \left( \begin{array}{ccc|ccc} 1 & 2 & 3 & \tfrac{1}{2} & 0 & 0 \\ 0 & 0 & 1 & -\tfrac{1}{2} & 1 & 0 \\ 0 & 0 & -10 & -\tfrac{5}{2} & 0 & 1 \end{array} \right)$$

The usual strategy for row-reduction has created a leading 1 in the second row that does not lie on the leading diagonal of the left half. Hence the left half cannot reduce to $\mathbf{I}$, and therefore the given matrix is not invertible.

**4.5** The matrix form of the system is

$$\left( \begin{array}{ccc} 1 & 1 & 2 \\ -1 & 0 & -4 \\ 3 & 2 & 10 \end{array} \right) \left( \begin{array}{c} x \\ y \\ z \end{array} \right) = \left( \begin{array}{c} 1 \\ 2 \\ -1 \end{array} \right).$$

Multiplying this equation on the left by the inverse of the coefficient matrix gives the solution

$$\left( \begin{array}{c} x \\ y \\ z \end{array} \right) = \left( \begin{array}{ccc} 4 & -3 & -2 \\ -1 & 2 & 1 \\ -1 & \tfrac{1}{2} & \tfrac{1}{2} \end{array} \right) \left( \begin{array}{c} 1 \\ 2 \\ -1 \end{array} \right) = \left( \begin{array}{c} 0 \\ 2 \\ -\tfrac{1}{2} \end{array} \right);$$

that is, $x = 0$, $y = 2$, $z = -\tfrac{1}{2}$.

**4.6**

**(a)**

$$\underbrace{\left( \begin{array}{cc} 5 & 0 \\ 0 & 1 \end{array} \right)}_{\substack{\text{elementary} \\ \text{matrix} \\ \text{associated with} \\ \mathbf{r}_1 \to 5\mathbf{r}_1}} \underbrace{\left( \begin{array}{ccc} 1 & 2 & 3 \\ 3 & 2 & 1 \end{array} \right)}_{\mathbf{A}} = \underbrace{\left( \begin{array}{ccc} 5 & 10 & 15 \\ 3 & 2 & 1 \end{array} \right)}_{\substack{\text{matrix} \\ \text{obtained when} \\ \mathbf{r}_1 \to 5\mathbf{r}_1 \\ \text{is performed on } \mathbf{A}}}$$

**(b)**

$$\underbrace{\left( \begin{array}{cccc} 1 & 0 & 0 & 0 \\ 0 & 1 & 0 & 3 \\ 0 & 0 & 1 & 0 \\ 0 & 0 & 0 & 1 \end{array} \right)}_{\substack{\text{elementary} \\ \text{matrix} \\ \text{associated with} \\ \mathbf{r}_2 \to \mathbf{r}_2 + 3\mathbf{r}_4}} \underbrace{\left( \begin{array}{cc} 1 & 2 \\ 3 & 4 \\ 5 & 6 \\ 7 & 8 \end{array} \right)}_{\mathbf{B}} = \underbrace{\left( \begin{array}{cc} 1 & 2 \\ 24 & 28 \\ 5 & 6 \\ 7 & 8 \end{array} \right)}_{\substack{\text{matrix} \\ \text{obtained when} \\ \mathbf{r}_2 \to \mathbf{r}_2 + 3\mathbf{r}_4 \\ \text{is performed on } \mathbf{B}}}$$

**4.7 (a)** The inverse elementary row operation of $\mathbf{r}_1 \to \mathbf{r}_1 - 2\mathbf{r}_2$ is $\mathbf{r}_1 \to \mathbf{r}_1 + 2\mathbf{r}_2$.

The working below shows the sequence of two row operations performed on the given matrix.

$$\begin{array}{c}\mathbf{r}_1 \\ \mathbf{r}_2\end{array} \quad \begin{pmatrix} 1 & 2 & 3 \\ 4 & 5 & 6 \end{pmatrix}$$

$$\mathbf{r}_1 \to \mathbf{r}_1 - 2\mathbf{r}_2 \quad \begin{pmatrix} -7 & -8 & -9 \\ 4 & 5 & 6 \end{pmatrix}$$

$$\mathbf{r}_1 \to \mathbf{r}_1 + 2\mathbf{r}_2 \quad \begin{pmatrix} 1 & 2 & 3 \\ 4 & 5 & 6 \end{pmatrix}$$

**(b)** The inverse elementary row operation of $\mathbf{r}_1 \leftrightarrow \mathbf{r}_2$ is $\mathbf{r}_1 \leftrightarrow \mathbf{r}_2$.

The working below shows the sequence of two row operations performed on the given matrix.

$$\begin{array}{c}\mathbf{r}_1 \\ \mathbf{r}_2\end{array} \quad \begin{pmatrix} 1 & 2 & 3 \\ 4 & 5 & 6 \end{pmatrix}$$

$$\mathbf{r}_1 \leftrightarrow \mathbf{r}_2 \quad \begin{pmatrix} 4 & 5 & 6 \\ 1 & 2 & 3 \end{pmatrix}$$

$$\mathbf{r}_1 \leftrightarrow \mathbf{r}_2 \quad \begin{pmatrix} 1 & 2 & 3 \\ 4 & 5 & 6 \end{pmatrix}$$

**(c)** The inverse elementary row operation of $\mathbf{r}_2 \to -3\mathbf{r}_2$ is $\mathbf{r}_2 \to -\frac{1}{3}\mathbf{r}_2$.

The working below shows the sequence of two row operations performed on the given matrix.

$$\begin{array}{c}\mathbf{r}_1 \\ \mathbf{r}_2\end{array} \quad \begin{pmatrix} 1 & 2 & 3 \\ 4 & 5 & 6 \end{pmatrix}$$

$$\mathbf{r}_2 \to -3\mathbf{r}_2 \quad \begin{pmatrix} 1 & 2 & 3 \\ -12 & -15 & -18 \end{pmatrix}$$

$$\mathbf{r}_2 \to -\frac{1}{3}\mathbf{r}_2 \quad \begin{pmatrix} 1 & 2 & 3 \\ 4 & 5 & 6 \end{pmatrix}$$

**4.8** The given matrix has associated elementary row operation $\mathbf{r}_1 \to 2\mathbf{r}_1$, which has inverse $\mathbf{r}_1 \to \frac{1}{2}\mathbf{r}_1$. The inverse of the given matrix is the elementary matrix associated with this inverse row operation, which is

$$\begin{pmatrix} \frac{1}{2} & 0 & 0 \\ 0 & 1 & 0 \\ 0 & 0 & 1 \end{pmatrix}.$$

**4.9** To prove that $k\mathbf{A}$ is invertible, with inverse $(1/k)\mathbf{A}^{-1}$, we have to show that

$$(k\mathbf{A})\left(\frac{1}{k}\mathbf{A}^{-1}\right) = \mathbf{I} \quad \text{and} \quad \left(\frac{1}{k}\mathbf{A}^{-1}\right)(k\mathbf{A}) = \mathbf{I}.$$

But

$$(k\mathbf{A})\left(\frac{1}{k}\mathbf{A}^{-1}\right) = \left(k \times \frac{1}{k}\right)(\mathbf{A}\mathbf{A}^{-1}) = 1\mathbf{I} = \mathbf{I},$$

and

$$\left(\frac{1}{k}\mathbf{A}^{-1}\right)(k\mathbf{A}) = \left(\frac{1}{k} \times k\right)(\mathbf{A}^{-1}\mathbf{A}) = 1\mathbf{I} = \mathbf{I},$$

as required.

**4.10 (a)** We row-reduce $(\mathbf{A} \mid \mathbf{I})$.

$$\begin{array}{c}\mathbf{r}_1 \\ \mathbf{r}_2\end{array} \quad \left(\begin{array}{cc|cc} 2 & 3 & 1 & 0 \\ 3 & 5 & 0 & 1 \end{array}\right)$$

$$\mathbf{r}_1 \to \frac{1}{2}\mathbf{r}_1 \quad \left(\begin{array}{cc|cc} 1 & \frac{3}{2} & \frac{1}{2} & 0 \\ 3 & 5 & 0 & 1 \end{array}\right)$$

$$\mathbf{r}_2 \to \mathbf{r}_2 - 3\mathbf{r}_1 \quad \left(\begin{array}{cc|cc} 1 & \frac{3}{2} & \frac{1}{2} & 0 \\ 0 & \frac{1}{2} & -\frac{3}{2} & 1 \end{array}\right)$$

$$\mathbf{r}_2 \to 2\mathbf{r}_2$$

$$\mathbf{r}_1 \to \mathbf{r}_1 - \frac{3}{2}\mathbf{r}_2 \quad \left(\begin{array}{cc|cc} 1 & 0 & 5 & -3 \\ 0 & 1 & -3 & 2 \end{array}\right)$$

The left half has been reduced to $\mathbf{I}$, so the given matrix is invertible; its inverse is

$$\begin{pmatrix} 5 & -3 \\ -3 & 2 \end{pmatrix}.$$

**(b)** We row-reduce $(\mathbf{A} \mid \mathbf{I})$.

$$\begin{array}{c}\mathbf{r}_1 \\ \mathbf{r}_2\end{array} \quad \left(\begin{array}{cc|cc} -2 & 4 & 1 & 0 \\ 3 & -6 & 0 & 1 \end{array}\right)$$

$$\mathbf{r}_1 \to -\frac{1}{2}\mathbf{r}_1 \quad \left(\begin{array}{cc|cc} 1 & -2 & -\frac{1}{2} & 0 \\ 3 & -6 & 0 & 1 \end{array}\right)$$

$$\mathbf{r}_2 \to \mathbf{r}_2 - 3\mathbf{r}_1 \quad \left(\begin{array}{cc|cc} 1 & -2 & -\frac{1}{2} & 0 \\ 0 & 0 & \frac{3}{2} & 1 \end{array}\right)$$

The left half is now in row-reduced form, but it is not the identity matrix. Therefore the given matrix is not invertible.

**(c)** We row-reduce $(\mathbf{A} \mid \mathbf{I})$.

$$\begin{array}{c}\mathbf{r}_1 \\ \mathbf{r}_2 \\ \mathbf{r}_3\end{array} \quad \left(\begin{array}{ccc|ccc} 1 & 2 & 4 & 1 & 0 & 0 \\ -2 & -1 & 1 & 0 & 1 & 0 \\ 1 & 1 & 1 & 0 & 0 & 1 \end{array}\right)$$

$$\begin{array}{c}\mathbf{r}_2 \to \mathbf{r}_2 + 2\mathbf{r}_1 \\ \mathbf{r}_3 \to \mathbf{r}_3 - \mathbf{r}_1\end{array} \quad \left(\begin{array}{ccc|ccc} 1 & 2 & 4 & 1 & 0 & 0 \\ 0 & 3 & 9 & 2 & 1 & 0 \\ 0 & -1 & -3 & -1 & 0 & 1 \end{array}\right)$$

$$\mathbf{r}_2 \to \frac{1}{3}\mathbf{r}_2 \quad \left(\begin{array}{ccc|ccc} 1 & 2 & 4 & 1 & 0 & 0 \\ 0 & 1 & 3 & \frac{2}{3} & \frac{1}{3} & 0 \\ 0 & -1 & -3 & -1 & 0 & 1 \end{array}\right)$$

$$\begin{array}{c}\mathbf{r}_1 \to \mathbf{r}_1 - 2\mathbf{r}_2 \\ \\ \mathbf{r}_3 \to \mathbf{r}_3 + \mathbf{r}_2\end{array} \quad \left(\begin{array}{ccc|ccc} 1 & 0 & -2 & -\frac{1}{3} & -\frac{2}{3} & 0 \\ 0 & 1 & 3 & \frac{2}{3} & \frac{1}{3} & 0 \\ 0 & 0 & 0 & -\frac{1}{3} & \frac{1}{3} & 1 \end{array}\right)$$

The left half is now in row-reduced form, but it is not the identity matrix. Therefore the given matrix is not invertible.

(d)  We row-reduce $(\mathbf{A} \mid \mathbf{I})$.

$$
\begin{array}{c}
\mathbf{r}_1 \\
\mathbf{r}_2 \\
\mathbf{r}_3
\end{array}
\left(\begin{array}{ccc|ccc}
1 & 4 & 1 & 1 & 0 & 0 \\
1 & 6 & 3 & 0 & 1 & 0 \\
2 & 3 & 0 & 0 & 0 & 1
\end{array}\right)
$$

$$
\begin{array}{c}
\\
\mathbf{r}_2 \to \mathbf{r}_2 - \mathbf{r}_1 \\
\mathbf{r}_3 \to \mathbf{r}_3 - 2\mathbf{r}_1
\end{array}
\left(\begin{array}{ccc|ccc}
1 & 4 & 1 & 1 & 0 & 0 \\
0 & 2 & 2 & -1 & 1 & 0 \\
0 & -5 & -2 & -2 & 0 & 1
\end{array}\right)
$$

$$
\begin{array}{c}
\\
\mathbf{r}_2 \to \tfrac{1}{2}\mathbf{r}_2 \\
\\
\end{array}
\left(\begin{array}{ccc|ccc}
1 & 4 & 1 & 1 & 0 & 0 \\
0 & 1 & 1 & -\tfrac{1}{2} & \tfrac{1}{2} & 0 \\
0 & -5 & -2 & -2 & 0 & 1
\end{array}\right)
$$

$$
\begin{array}{c}
\mathbf{r}_1 \to \mathbf{r}_1 - 4\mathbf{r}_2 \\
\\
\mathbf{r}_3 \to \mathbf{r}_3 + 5\mathbf{r}_2
\end{array}
\left(\begin{array}{ccc|ccc}
1 & 0 & -3 & 3 & -2 & 0 \\
0 & 1 & 1 & -\tfrac{1}{2} & \tfrac{1}{2} & 0 \\
0 & 0 & 3 & -\tfrac{9}{2} & \tfrac{5}{2} & 1
\end{array}\right)
$$

$$
\begin{array}{c}
\\
\\
\mathbf{r}_3 \to \tfrac{1}{3}\mathbf{r}_3
\end{array}
\left(\begin{array}{ccc|ccc}
1 & 0 & -3 & 3 & -2 & 0 \\
0 & 1 & 1 & -\tfrac{1}{2} & \tfrac{1}{2} & 0 \\
0 & 0 & 1 & -\tfrac{3}{2} & \tfrac{5}{6} & \tfrac{1}{3}
\end{array}\right)
$$

$$
\begin{array}{c}
\mathbf{r}_1 \to \mathbf{r}_1 + 3\mathbf{r}_3 \\
\\
\mathbf{r}_2 \to \mathbf{r}_2 - \mathbf{r}_3
\end{array}
\left(\begin{array}{ccc|ccc}
1 & 0 & 0 & -\tfrac{3}{2} & \tfrac{1}{2} & 1 \\
0 & 1 & 0 & 1 & -\tfrac{1}{3} & -\tfrac{1}{3} \\
0 & 0 & 1 & -\tfrac{3}{2} & \tfrac{5}{6} & \tfrac{1}{3}
\end{array}\right)
$$

The left half has been reduced to $\mathbf{I}$, so the given matrix is invertible; its inverse is

$$
\begin{pmatrix}
-\tfrac{3}{2} & \tfrac{1}{2} & 1 \\
1 & -\tfrac{1}{3} & -\tfrac{1}{3} \\
-\tfrac{3}{2} & \tfrac{5}{6} & \tfrac{1}{3}
\end{pmatrix}.
$$

(e)  We row-reduce $(\mathbf{A} \mid \mathbf{I})$.

$$
\begin{array}{c}
\mathbf{r}_1 \\
\mathbf{r}_2 \\
\mathbf{r}_3 \\
\mathbf{r}_4
\end{array}
\left(\begin{array}{cccc|cccc}
1 & 0 & 0 & 3 & 1 & 0 & 0 & 0 \\
0 & 1 & 2 & 0 & 0 & 1 & 0 & 0 \\
0 & -1 & -1 & 0 & 0 & 0 & 1 & 0 \\
-1 & 0 & 0 & -2 & 0 & 0 & 0 & 1
\end{array}\right)
$$

$$
\begin{array}{c}
\\
\\
\\
\mathbf{r}_4 \to \mathbf{r}_4 + \mathbf{r}_1
\end{array}
\left(\begin{array}{cccc|cccc}
1 & 0 & 0 & 3 & 1 & 0 & 0 & 0 \\
0 & 1 & 2 & 0 & 0 & 1 & 0 & 0 \\
0 & -1 & -1 & 0 & 0 & 0 & 1 & 0 \\
0 & 0 & 0 & 1 & 1 & 0 & 0 & 1
\end{array}\right)
$$

$$
\begin{array}{c}
\\
\\
\mathbf{r}_3 \to \mathbf{r}_3 + \mathbf{r}_2 \\
\\
\end{array}
\left(\begin{array}{cccc|cccc}
1 & 0 & 0 & 3 & 1 & 0 & 0 & 0 \\
0 & 1 & 2 & 0 & 0 & 1 & 0 & 0 \\
0 & 0 & 1 & 0 & 0 & 1 & 1 & 0 \\
0 & 0 & 0 & 1 & 1 & 0 & 0 & 1
\end{array}\right)
$$

$$
\begin{array}{c}
\\
\mathbf{r}_2 \to \mathbf{r}_2 - 2\mathbf{r}_3 \\
\\
\\
\end{array}
\left(\begin{array}{cccc|cccc}
1 & 0 & 0 & 3 & 1 & 0 & 0 & 0 \\
0 & 1 & 0 & 0 & 0 & -1 & -2 & 0 \\
0 & 0 & 1 & 0 & 0 & 1 & 1 & 0 \\
0 & 0 & 0 & 1 & 1 & 0 & 0 & 1
\end{array}\right)
$$

$$
\begin{array}{c}
\mathbf{r}_1 \to \mathbf{r}_1 - 3\mathbf{r}_4 \\
\\
\\
\\
\end{array}
\left(\begin{array}{cccc|cccc}
1 & 0 & 0 & 0 & -2 & 0 & 0 & -3 \\
0 & 1 & 0 & 0 & 0 & -1 & -2 & 0 \\
0 & 0 & 1 & 0 & 0 & 1 & 1 & 0 \\
0 & 0 & 0 & 1 & 1 & 0 & 0 & 1
\end{array}\right)
$$

The left half has been reduced to $\mathbf{I}$, so the given matrix is invertible; its inverse is

$$
\begin{pmatrix}
-2 & 0 & 0 & -3 \\
0 & -1 & -2 & 0 \\
0 & 1 & 1 & 0 \\
1 & 0 & 0 & 1
\end{pmatrix}.
$$

**4.11** (a)  The matrix form of the system is

$$
\begin{pmatrix} 2 & 3 \\ 3 & 5 \end{pmatrix} \begin{pmatrix} x \\ y \end{pmatrix} = \begin{pmatrix} 3 \\ 4 \end{pmatrix}.
$$

Multiplying this equation on the left by the inverse of the coefficient matrix (from Exercise 4.10(a)) gives the solution

$$
\begin{pmatrix} x \\ y \end{pmatrix} = \begin{pmatrix} 5 & -3 \\ -3 & 2 \end{pmatrix} \begin{pmatrix} 3 \\ 4 \end{pmatrix} = \begin{pmatrix} 3 \\ -1 \end{pmatrix};
$$

that is, $x = 3$, $y = -1$.

(b)  The matrix form of the system is

$$
\begin{pmatrix} 1 & 4 & 1 \\ 1 & 6 & 3 \\ 2 & 3 & 0 \end{pmatrix} \begin{pmatrix} x_1 \\ x_2 \\ x_3 \end{pmatrix} = \begin{pmatrix} 4 \\ 6 \\ 9 \end{pmatrix}.
$$

Multiplying this equation on the left by the inverse of the coefficient matrix (from Exercise 4.10(d)) gives the solution

$$
\begin{pmatrix} x_1 \\ x_2 \\ x_3 \end{pmatrix} = \begin{pmatrix} -\tfrac{3}{2} & \tfrac{1}{2} & 1 \\ 1 & -\tfrac{1}{3} & -\tfrac{1}{3} \\ -\tfrac{3}{2} & \tfrac{5}{6} & \tfrac{1}{3} \end{pmatrix} \begin{pmatrix} 4 \\ 6 \\ 9 \end{pmatrix} = \begin{pmatrix} 6 \\ -1 \\ 2 \end{pmatrix};
$$

that is, $x_1 = 6$, $x_2 = -1$, $x_3 = 2$.

**4.12** (a)  Let $\mathbf{A}$ be an $n \times n$ matrix.

Every elementary matrix is invertible (by the corollary to Theorem 4.9), and the product of invertible matrices is invertible (by Theorem 4.3). So if $\mathbf{A}$ can be expressed as a product of elementary matrices, then $\mathbf{A}$ is invertible.

For the converse, suppose that $\mathbf{A}$ is invertible. Then, by the Invertibility Theorem, the row-reduced form of $\mathbf{A}$ is $\mathbf{I}$. Let $\mathbf{E}_1, \mathbf{E}_2, \ldots, \mathbf{E}_k$ be the $n \times n$ elementary matrices associated with a sequence of elementary row operations that transforms $\mathbf{A}$ to $\mathbf{I}$, in the same order. Then, by the corollary to Theorem 4.8,

$$\mathbf{I} = \mathbf{B}\mathbf{A},$$

where $\mathbf{B} = \mathbf{E}_k \mathbf{E}_{k-1} \cdots \mathbf{E}_2 \mathbf{E}_1$. Now $\mathbf{B}$ is a product of invertible matrices, and is therefore itself an invertible matrix. Multiplying both sides of the above equation on the left by $\mathbf{B}^{-1}$ yields

$$\mathbf{B}^{-1}\mathbf{I} = \mathbf{B}^{-1}\mathbf{B}\mathbf{A},$$

that is,

$$\mathbf{B}^{-1} = \mathbf{A}.$$

So

$$(\mathbf{E}_k \mathbf{E}_{k-1} \cdots \mathbf{E}_2 \mathbf{E}_1)^{-1} = \mathbf{A},$$

which, by Theorem 4.3, is equivalent to

$$\mathbf{E}_1^{-1} \mathbf{E}_2^{-1} \cdots \mathbf{E}_k^{-1} = \mathbf{A}.$$

By the corollary to Theorem 4.9, the inverse of every elementary matrix is an elementary matrix, and so this expresses $\mathbf{A}$ as a product of elementary matrices.

(b) Let $\mathbf{A}$ be the matrix in Exercise 4.10(a). It is transformed to $\mathbf{I}$ by the sequence of elementary row operations $\mathbf{r}_1 \to \frac{1}{2}\mathbf{r}_1$, $\mathbf{r}_2 \to \mathbf{r}_2 - 3\mathbf{r}_1$, $\mathbf{r}_2 \to 2\mathbf{r}_2$, $\mathbf{r}_1 \to \mathbf{r}_1 - \frac{3}{2}\mathbf{r}_2$ (see the solution to Exercise 4.10(a)). Therefore, by the argument in part (a) above,

$$\mathbf{A} = \begin{pmatrix} \frac{1}{2} & 0 \\ 0 & 1 \end{pmatrix}^{-1} \begin{pmatrix} 1 & 0 \\ -3 & 1 \end{pmatrix}^{-1} \begin{pmatrix} 1 & 0 \\ 0 & 2 \end{pmatrix}^{-1} \begin{pmatrix} 1 & -\frac{3}{2} \\ 0 & 1 \end{pmatrix}^{-1}$$

$$= \begin{pmatrix} 2 & 0 \\ 0 & 1 \end{pmatrix} \begin{pmatrix} 1 & 0 \\ 3 & 1 \end{pmatrix} \begin{pmatrix} 1 & 0 \\ 0 & \frac{1}{2} \end{pmatrix} \begin{pmatrix} 1 & \frac{3}{2} \\ 0 & 1 \end{pmatrix}.$$

(The inverses of the elementary matrices are easily found using the argument in the proof of the corollary to Theorem 4.9.)

Using a different sequence of row operations to row-reduce $\mathbf{A}$ would lead to a different way of expressing $\mathbf{A}$ as a product of elementary matrices—so your solution may differ from the one above.

**5.1 (a)** $\begin{vmatrix} 5 & 1 \\ 4 & 2 \end{vmatrix} = (5 \times 2) - (1 \times 4) = 6$

**(b)** $\begin{vmatrix} 10 & -4 \\ -5 & 2 \end{vmatrix} = (10 \times 2) - (-4 \times -5) = 0$

**(c)** $\begin{vmatrix} 7 & 3 \\ 17 & 2 \end{vmatrix} = (7 \times 2) - (3 \times 17) = -37$

**5.2 (a)** First we evaluate the determinant of the matrix:
$$\begin{vmatrix} 4 & 2 \\ 5 & 6 \end{vmatrix} = (4 \times 6) - (2 \times 5) = 14.$$

This determinant is non-zero, so the matrix is invertible. We use the formula to find the inverse:
$$\begin{pmatrix} 4 & 2 \\ 5 & 6 \end{pmatrix}^{-1} = \frac{1}{14}\begin{pmatrix} 6 & -2 \\ -5 & 4 \end{pmatrix} = \begin{pmatrix} \frac{3}{7} & -\frac{1}{7} \\ -\frac{5}{14} & \frac{2}{7} \end{pmatrix}.$$

**(b)** First we evaluate the determinant of the matrix:
$$\begin{vmatrix} 1 & 1 \\ -1 & 1 \end{vmatrix} = (1 \times 1) - (1 \times -1) = 2.$$

This determinant is non-zero, so the matrix is invertible. We use the formula to find the inverse:
$$\begin{pmatrix} 1 & 1 \\ -1 & 1 \end{pmatrix}^{-1} = \frac{1}{2}\begin{pmatrix} 1 & -1 \\ 1 & 1 \end{pmatrix} = \begin{pmatrix} \frac{1}{2} & -\frac{1}{2} \\ \frac{1}{2} & \frac{1}{2} \end{pmatrix}.$$

**(c)** First we evaluate the determinant of the matrix:
$$\begin{vmatrix} 1 & -1 \\ -1 & 1 \end{vmatrix} = (1 \times 1) - (-1 \times -1) = 0.$$

This determinant is 0, so the matrix is not invertible.

**5.3 (a)** $\begin{vmatrix} 3 & 2 & 1 \\ 4 & 0 & -1 \\ 0 & -1 & 1 \end{vmatrix}$

$$= 3\begin{vmatrix} 0 & -1 \\ -1 & 1 \end{vmatrix} - 2\begin{vmatrix} 4 & -1 \\ 0 & 1 \end{vmatrix} + 1\begin{vmatrix} 4 & 0 \\ 0 & -1 \end{vmatrix}$$

$$= 3((0 \times 1) - (-1 \times -1)) - 2((4 \times 1) - (-1 \times 0))$$
$$\quad + ((4 \times -1) - (0 \times 0))$$

$$= -15$$

**(b)** $\begin{vmatrix} 2 & 10 & 0 \\ 3 & -1 & 2 \\ 5 & 9 & 2 \end{vmatrix} = 2\begin{vmatrix} -1 & 2 \\ 9 & 2 \end{vmatrix} - 10\begin{vmatrix} 3 & 2 \\ 5 & 2 \end{vmatrix} + 0$

$$= 2((-1 \times 2) - (2 \times 9))$$
$$\quad - 10(3 \times 2) - (2 \times 5))$$

$$= 0$$

**5.4** The cofactor $A_{13}$ is $(-1)^{1+3} = (-1)^4 = 1$ times the determinant of the matrix obtained by covering up the top row and third column of $\mathbf{A}$:

$$A_{13} = \begin{vmatrix} 2 & 3 & 5 & 1 \\ 3 & 4 & 1 & 2 \\ 4 & 5 & 2 & 3 \\ 5 & 1 & 3 & 4 \end{vmatrix}.$$

The cofactor $A_{45}$ is $(-1)^{4+5} = (-1)^9 = -1$ times the determinant of the matrix obtained by covering up the fourth row and fifth column of $\mathbf{A}$:

$$A_{45} = (-1)\begin{vmatrix} 1 & 2 & 3 & 4 \\ 2 & 3 & 4 & 5 \\ 3 & 4 & 5 & 1 \\ 5 & 1 & 2 & 3 \end{vmatrix}.$$

**5.5** We apply Strategy 5.2:
$$\begin{vmatrix} 0 & 2 & 1 & -1 \\ -3 & 0 & 0 & -1 \\ 1 & 0 & 1 & 0 \\ 0 & 4 & 2 & 0 \end{vmatrix}$$

$$= 0 - 2\begin{vmatrix} -3 & 0 & -1 \\ 1 & 1 & 0 \\ 0 & 2 & 0 \end{vmatrix} + \begin{vmatrix} -3 & 0 & -1 \\ 1 & 0 & 0 \\ 0 & 4 & 0 \end{vmatrix}$$

$$\quad - (-1)\begin{vmatrix} -3 & 0 & 0 \\ 1 & 0 & 1 \\ 0 & 4 & 2 \end{vmatrix}$$

$$= -2\left(-3\begin{vmatrix} 1 & 0 \\ 2 & 0 \end{vmatrix} - 0 + (-1)\begin{vmatrix} 1 & 1 \\ 0 & 2 \end{vmatrix}\right)$$

$$\quad + \left(-3\begin{vmatrix} 0 & 0 \\ 4 & 0 \end{vmatrix} - 0 + (-1)\begin{vmatrix} 1 & 0 \\ 0 & 4 \end{vmatrix}\right)$$

$$\quad + \left(-3\begin{vmatrix} 0 & 1 \\ 4 & 2 \end{vmatrix} - 0 + 0\right)$$

$$= (-2)(-2) + (-1)4 + (-3)(-4)$$

$$= 12.$$

**5.6** Here,

$$\det \mathbf{A} = \begin{vmatrix} -3 & 1 \\ 2 & -4 \end{vmatrix}$$

$$= (-3 \times -4) - (1 \times 2) = 10,$$

$$\det \mathbf{B} = \begin{vmatrix} 1 & 1 \\ -2 & 5 \end{vmatrix}$$

$$= (1 \times 5) - (1 \times -2) = 7$$

and

$$\mathbf{A} + \mathbf{B} = \begin{pmatrix} -2 & 2 \\ 0 & 1 \end{pmatrix},$$

so

$$\det(\mathbf{A} + \mathbf{B}) = (-2 \times 1) - (2 \times 0) = -2.$$

We have $\det \mathbf{A} + \det \mathbf{B} = 10 + 7 = 17$, so $\det(\mathbf{A} + \mathbf{B})$ is not equal to $\det \mathbf{A} + \det \mathbf{B}$.

$$\mathbf{A}\mathbf{B} = \begin{pmatrix} -5 & 2 \\ 10 & -18 \end{pmatrix},$$

so

$$\det(\mathbf{A}\mathbf{B}) = (-5 \times -18) - (2 \times 10) = 70.$$

We have $(\det \mathbf{A})(\det \mathbf{B}) = 10 \times 7 = 70$, so

$$\det(\mathbf{A}\mathbf{B}) = (\det \mathbf{A})(\det \mathbf{B}).$$

**5.7** (a) We apply Strategy 5.2:

$$\begin{vmatrix} 0 & 1 & 0 \\ 1 & 0 & 0 \\ 0 & 0 & 1 \end{vmatrix} = 0 - \begin{vmatrix} 1 & 0 \\ 0 & 1 \end{vmatrix} + 0$$

$$= -1.$$

(b) We apply Strategy 5.2:

$$\begin{vmatrix} 1 & 0 & 0 & 0 \\ 0 & 1 & 0 & 0 \\ 0 & 0 & k & 0 \\ 0 & 0 & 0 & 1 \end{vmatrix} = \begin{vmatrix} 1 & 0 & 0 \\ 0 & k & 0 \\ 0 & 0 & 1 \end{vmatrix} - 0 + 0 - 0$$

$$= \begin{vmatrix} k & 0 \\ 0 & 1 \end{vmatrix} - 0 + 0$$

$$= (k \times 1) - (0 \times 0)$$

$$= k.$$

(c) We evaluate the determinant:

$$\begin{vmatrix} 1 & 0 \\ k & 1 \end{vmatrix} = (1 \times 1) - (0 \times k)$$

$$= 1.$$

**5.8** First notice that

$$-2 \begin{pmatrix} 1 & -2 & 4 \end{pmatrix} = \begin{pmatrix} -2 & 4 & -8 \end{pmatrix},$$

that is, the first and third rows of $\mathbf{A}$ are proportional. Therefore, by Theorem 5.3,

$$\det \mathbf{A} = 0.$$

**5.9** First notice that the third row of $\mathbf{A}$ has only one non-zero entry. We interchange the first and third rows, and apply Theorems 5.1 and 5.2, giving

$$\det \mathbf{A} = \begin{vmatrix} 10 & 3 & -4 & 2 \\ 0 & 2 & 0 & 1 \\ 0 & 6 & 0 & 0 \\ -1 & 2 & 1 & 0 \end{vmatrix} = (-1) \begin{vmatrix} 0 & 6 & 0 & 0 \\ 0 & 2 & 0 & 1 \\ 10 & 3 & -4 & 2 \\ -1 & 2 & 1 & 0 \end{vmatrix}.$$

We use Strategy 5.2 to evaluate this determinant:

$$\det \mathbf{A} = (-1) \left( 0 - 6 \begin{vmatrix} 0 & 0 & 1 \\ 10 & -4 & 2 \\ -1 & 1 & 0 \end{vmatrix} + 0 - 0 \right)$$

$$= 6 \left( 0 - 0 + \begin{vmatrix} 10 & -4 \\ -1 & 1 \end{vmatrix} \right)$$

$$= 6 \left( (10 \times 1) - (-4 \times -1) \right)$$

$$= 36.$$

**5.10** (a) $\det \mathbf{A} = \begin{vmatrix} 2 & 0 \\ 4 & 1 \end{vmatrix} = 2$

(b) $\det \mathbf{B} = \begin{vmatrix} 1 & -1 \\ -2 & 5 \end{vmatrix} = 3$

(c) $\det(\mathbf{A} + \mathbf{B}) = \begin{vmatrix} 3 & -1 \\ 2 & 6 \end{vmatrix} = 20$

(d) $\det(\mathbf{A}\mathbf{B}) = (\det \mathbf{A})(\det \mathbf{B}) = 6$

(e) $\det(\mathbf{B}\mathbf{A}) = (\det \mathbf{B})(\det \mathbf{A}) = 6$

(f) $\det(\mathbf{A}^2) = (\det \mathbf{A})^2 = 4$

(g) $\det \mathbf{A}^T = \det \mathbf{A} = 2$

(h) $\det(\mathbf{A}\mathbf{B})^T = \det(\mathbf{A}\mathbf{B}) = 6$

(i) Since $\det \mathbf{A} \neq 0$,

$$\det \mathbf{A}^{-1} = 1/(\det \mathbf{A}) = \tfrac{1}{2}.$$

**5.11** (a) We first evaluate the determinant of the matrix:

$$\begin{vmatrix} 2 & 1 \\ 1 & 2 \end{vmatrix} = 3.$$

This determinant is non-zero, so the matrix is invertible. The inverse is

$$\begin{pmatrix} 2 & 1 \\ 1 & 2 \end{pmatrix}^{-1} = \tfrac{1}{3} \begin{pmatrix} 2 & -1 \\ -1 & 2 \end{pmatrix} = \begin{pmatrix} \tfrac{2}{3} & -\tfrac{1}{3} \\ -\tfrac{1}{3} & \tfrac{2}{3} \end{pmatrix}.$$

(b) We first evaluate the determinant of the matrix:

$$\begin{vmatrix} 2 & -2 \\ -1 & 1 \end{vmatrix} = 0.$$

This determinant is zero, so the matrix is not invertible.

(c) We first evaluate the determinant of the matrix:

$$\begin{vmatrix} 10 & 21 \\ -4 & -7 \end{vmatrix} = 14.$$

This determinant is non-zero, so the matrix is invertible. The inverse is

$$\begin{pmatrix} 10 & 21 \\ -4 & -7 \end{pmatrix}^{-1} = \tfrac{1}{14} \begin{pmatrix} -7 & -21 \\ 4 & 10 \end{pmatrix}$$

$$= \begin{pmatrix} -\tfrac{1}{2} & -\tfrac{3}{2} \\ \tfrac{2}{7} & \tfrac{5}{7} \end{pmatrix}.$$

**5.12** (a) Here, the first and third columns are proportional, since

$$2\begin{pmatrix} 5 \\ -1 \\ 2 \\ 3 \end{pmatrix} = \begin{pmatrix} 10 \\ -2 \\ 4 \\ 6 \end{pmatrix}.$$

The determinant is therefore zero, by Theorem 5.3.

(b) First notice that the third row has only one non-zero entry. We interchange the first and third rows, and apply Theorems 5.1 and 5.2, giving

$$\begin{vmatrix} 7 & 10 & -1 & 0 & 2 \\ 1 & 5 & 0 & 2 & 0 \\ 0 & 2 & 0 & 0 & 0 \\ 3 & -6 & 3 & 7 & 1 \\ 3 & 4 & 3 & 0 & 1 \end{vmatrix}$$

$$= (-1)\begin{vmatrix} 0 & 2 & 0 & 0 & 0 \\ 1 & 5 & 0 & 2 & 0 \\ 7 & 10 & -1 & 0 & 2 \\ 3 & -6 & 3 & 7 & 1 \\ 3 & 4 & 3 & 0 & 1 \end{vmatrix}$$

$$= (-1)(-2)\begin{vmatrix} 1 & 0 & 2 & 0 \\ 7 & -1 & 0 & 2 \\ 3 & 3 & 7 & 1 \\ 3 & 3 & 0 & 1 \end{vmatrix}$$

$$= 2\left( \begin{vmatrix} -1 & 0 & 2 \\ 3 & 7 & 1 \\ 3 & 0 & 1 \end{vmatrix} + 2\begin{vmatrix} 7 & -1 & 2 \\ 3 & 3 & 1 \\ 3 & 3 & 1 \end{vmatrix} \right)$$

$$= 2\left( -1\begin{vmatrix} 7 & 1 \\ 0 & 1 \end{vmatrix} + 2\begin{vmatrix} 3 & 7 \\ 3 & 0 \end{vmatrix} + 0 \right)$$

$$= 2(-7 - 42)$$

$$= -98.$$

Notice that the second $3 \times 3$ determinant vanishes, by Theorem 5.3, since the second and third rows are equal.

**5.13** In each part, we evaluate the determinant to determine whether or not the matrix is invertible.

(a) $\begin{vmatrix} 2 & 1 & 4 \\ 1 & -1 & 3 \\ -2 & 1 & 5 \end{vmatrix}$

$$= 2\begin{vmatrix} -1 & 3 \\ 1 & 5 \end{vmatrix} - \begin{vmatrix} 1 & 3 \\ -2 & 5 \end{vmatrix} + 4\begin{vmatrix} 1 & -1 \\ -2 & 1 \end{vmatrix}$$

$$= -16 - 11 - 4$$

$$= -31.$$

The determinant of this matrix is non-zero, so the matrix is invertible.

(b) By Theorem 5.3, the determinant is zero, since the first and third columns are equal. The matrix is therefore not invertible.

(c) $\begin{vmatrix} 1 & 0 & 0 & 0 \\ 2 & 1 & 0 & 0 \\ 3 & 2 & 1 & 0 \\ 4 & 3 & 2 & 1 \end{vmatrix} = \begin{vmatrix} 1 & 0 & 0 \\ 2 & 1 & 0 \\ 3 & 2 & 1 \end{vmatrix} = \begin{vmatrix} 1 & 0 \\ 2 & 1 \end{vmatrix} = 1.$

The determinant is non-zero, so the matrix is invertible.

**5.14** We first assume that $\mathbf{A}\mathbf{A}^T$ is invertible. By Theorem 5.4, $\det(\mathbf{A}\mathbf{A}^T)$ is non-zero, and by Theorem 5.1,

$$\det(\mathbf{A}\mathbf{A}^T) = (\det \mathbf{A})(\det \mathbf{A}^T).$$

So $\det \mathbf{A}$ and $\det \mathbf{A}^T$ are also non-zero, and therefore $\mathbf{A}$ and $\mathbf{A}^T$ are both invertible.

We now assume, for the converse, that $\mathbf{A}$ is invertible. Then $\det \mathbf{A}$ and $\det \mathbf{A}^T$ are non-zero, by Theorems 5.1 and 5.4, so

$$(\det \mathbf{A})(\det \mathbf{A}^T) = \det(\mathbf{A}\mathbf{A}^T) \neq 0.$$

So $\mathbf{A}\mathbf{A}^T$ is invertible, as required.

# Index